The 100 Word Exercise Book

sian

ıne Wi

ɔdi Ratıee

g-and-w PUBLISHING

Published by *g-and-w* PUBLISHING
47a High Street
Chinnor
Oxfordshire OX9 4DJ

First published 2003

ISBN 1-903103-09-6

Designed by: Robert Bowers

Illustrated by: Mahmoud Gaafar

Printed in Hong Kong
by Wing King Tong Co. Ltd.

1 2 3 4 5 6 7 8 9 09 08 07 06 05 04 03

Contents

INTRODUCTION

In this activity book you'll find 100 key words for you to learn to read in Persian. All the activities are designed specifically for reading non-Latin script languages. Many of the activities are inspired by the kind of games used to teach children to read their own language: flashcards, matching games, memory games, joining exercises, etc. This is not only a more effective method of learning to read a new script, but also much more fun.

We've included a **Scriptbreaker** to get you started. This is a friendly introduction to the Persian script that will give you tips on how to remember the letters.

Then you can move on to the eight **Topics**. Each topic presents essential words in large type. There is also a pronunciation guide so you know how to say the words. These words are also featured in the tear-out **Flashcard** section at the back of the book. When you've mastered the words, you can go on to try out the activities and games for that topic.

There's also a **Round-up** section to review all your new words and the **Answers** to all the activities to check yourself.

Follow this 4-step plan for maximum success:

1 Have a look at the key topic words with their pictures. Then tear out the flashcards and shuffle them. Put them Persian side up. Try to remember what the word means and turn the card over to check with the English. When you can do this, cover the pronunciation and try to say the word and remember the meaning by looking at the Persian script only.

2 Put the cards English side up and try to say the Persian word. Try the cards again each day both ways around. (When you can remember a card for seven days in a row, you can file it.)

3 Try out the activities and games for each topic. This will reinforce your recognition of the key words.

4 After you have covered all the topics, you can try the activities in the **Round-up** section to test your knowledge of all the 100 words in the book. You can also try shuffling all the flashcards together to see how many you can remember.

This flexible and fun way of reading your first words in Persian should give you a head start whether you're learning at home or in a group.

Scriptbreaker

The purpose of this Scriptbreaker is to introduce you to the Persian script and how it is formed. You should not try to memorise the alphabet at this stage, nor try to write the letters yourself. Instead, have a quick look through this section and then move on to the topics, glancing back if you want to work out the letters in a particular word. Remember, though, that recognising the whole shape of the word in an unfamiliar script is just as important as knowing how it is made up. Using this method you will have a much more instinctive recall of vocabulary and will gain the confidence to expand your knowledge in other directions.

Persian, also known as Farsi, is written in the Arabic script with some modified characters. Reading the script is not nearly as difficult as it might seem at first glance. There are 32 letters, no capital letters, and, unlike English, words are generally spelled as they sound. There are two main points to etch into your brain:

- Persian is written from right to left.
- The letters are "joined up" — you cannot "print" a word as you can in English.

The alphabet

The easiest way of tackling the alphabet is to divide it into similarly shaped letters. For example, here are two groups of similar letters. The only difference between them is the dots:

ح (the letter *he-jeemee*)	ب (the letter *beh*)
ج (the letter *jeem*)	ت (the letter *teh*)
خ (the letter *kheh*)	ث (the letter *seh*)
چ (the letter *cheh*)	پ (the letter *peh*)

When these letters join to other letters they change their shape. The most common change is that they lose their "tails":

ت + ج = تج   ح + ب = حب (read from *right to left*)

Because letters change their shape like this, they have an *initial*, a *medial* (middle) and a *final* form. For example, the letter ج (*jeem*) changes like this:

at the beginning of a word (*initial*)	جـ...
in the middle of a word (*medial*)	...ـجـ...
at the end of a word (*final*)	...ـج

بله

- ✔ Persian has 32 letters and no capital letters
- ✔ Persian reads right to left
- ✔ Persian is written in "joined up" writing
- ✔ The "tail" is generally chopped off before joining to the next letter

A few letters change their shapes completely depending on where they fall in a word. For example, the letter ه (*heh-do-chesm*) changes like this:

initial	هـ...
medial	...ـهـ...
final	...ـه

In addition, there are seven letters which *never* join to the letter *following* (to their left) and so hardly change shape at all. These are:

و (*vaav*)	ا (*alef*)	
د (*daal*)	ذ (*zaal*)	
ر (*reh*)	ز (*zeh*)	ژ (*zheh*)

You will find more details of how the individual letters change their shape in the table on page 8.

Formation of words

We can use the principles of joining letters to form words.

So, for example, the Persian word for "hotel" is the same as English and written like this:

(*hotel*) هتل = (*l*) ل + (*t*) ت + (*h*) ه ←

The Persian word for "sock" (*jooraab*), contains three non-joining letters and is written like this:

(*jooraab*) جوراب = (*b*) ب + (*aa*) ا + (*r*) ر + (*oo*) و + (*j*) ج ←

You may have noticed that some of the vowels seem to be missing from the script. In modern Persian, the short vowels (*a*, *e*, *o*) are not written as part of the script but as vowel signs above or below the letter. The short *a* is written as a dash above the letter (ـَ); the short *e* as a dash below (ـِ); and the short *o* as a comma-shape above (ـُ). This is similar to English shorthand, where we might write "bnk" instead of "bank". Here is "hotel" again, this time with the vowel signs:

هُتِل *(hotel)*

In this book we have included these vowel signs in the topics, but dropped them in the review section (*Round-up*). Most material for native speakers will leave them out as you are presumed to know them. This makes it all the more important for you to start recognising a word without the short vowels.

بله

- ✔ Persian letters have an *initial*, *medial* ("middle") and *final* form, depending on their position in the word
- ✔ Many Persian letters simply lose their tails for the *medial* and *final* form
- ✔ A few letters change their shape completely
- ✔ 7 letters don't join to the letter after and hardly change at all
- ✔ The short vowels (*a*, *e*, *o*) are written as vowel signs above and below the letter and are not usually included in modern Persian

Pronunciation tips

This activity book has simplified some aspects of pronunciation in order to emphasise the basics. Don't worry at this stage about being precisely correct – the other letters in a word will help you to be understood. Many Persian letters are pronounced in a similar way to their English equivalents, but here are a few that need special attention:

ق (*ghaaf*)/ غ (*ghein*)	both letters are pronounced like the French "r" as in "rue"
خ (*kheh*)	like the "ch" in the Scottish "loch" or the German "Bach"
ع (*ein*)	a glottal stop, similar to the sound made when "bottle" is pronounced with a cockney accent – *bo'le*

If you look at the alphabet table below, you will notice that a single sound can be represented by two or more letters. For example, the sound *t*, can be written with the letter ت (*teh*) or with the letter ط (*taa*).

Summary of the Persian alphabet

The table below shows all the Persian letters in the three positions, with the Persian letter name, followed by the sound. Remember that this is just for reference and you shouldn't expect to take it all in at once. If you know the basic principles of how the Persian script works, you will slowly come to recognise the individual letters.

	initial:	*medial:*	*final:*		*initial:*	*medial:*	*final:*		*initial:*	*medial:*	*final:*
alef *	ا	ـا	ا	reh *r*	ر	ـر	ر	feh *f*	فـ	ـفـ	ف
beh *b*	بـ	ـبـ	ب	zeh *z*	ز	ـز	ز	ghaaf *gh*	قـ	ـقـ	ق
peh *p*	پـ	ـپـ	پ	zheh *zh*	ژ	ـژ	ژ	kaaf *k*	کـ	ـکـ	ک
teh *t*	تـ	ـتـ	ت	seen *s*	سـ	ـسـ	س	gaaf *g*	گـ	ـگـ	گ
seh *s*	ثـ	ـثـ	ث	sheen *sh*	شـ	ـشـ	ش	laam *l*	لـ	ـلـ	ل
jeem *j*	جـ	ـجـ	ج	saad *s*	صـ	ـصـ	ص	meem *m*	مـ	ـمـ	م
cheh *ch*	چـ	ـچـ	چ	zaad *z*	ضـ	ـضـ	ض	noon *n*	نـ	ـنـ	ن
heh-jeemee *h*	حـ	ـحـ	ح	taa *t*	طـ	ـطـ	ط	vaav *v/oo/o*	و	ـو	و
kheh *kh*	خـ	ـخـ	خ	zaa *z*	ظـ	ـظـ	ظ	heh-do-chesm *h*	هـ	ـهـ	ه/ـه
daal *d*	د	ـد	د	ein ’	عـ	ـعـ	ع/ـع	yeh *y/ee*	یـ	ـیـ	ی
zaal *z*	ذ	ـذ	ذ	ghein *gh*	غـ	ـغـ	غ/ـغ				

* Any vowel in initial position and also *aa* in medial and final positions.

Note the special combination when *alef* is written after *laam*: لا, as in حالا (*haalaa*, meaning "now").

❶ Around the Home

Look at the pictures of things you might find in a house.
Tear out the flashcards for this topic.
Follow steps 1 and 2 of the plan in the introduction.

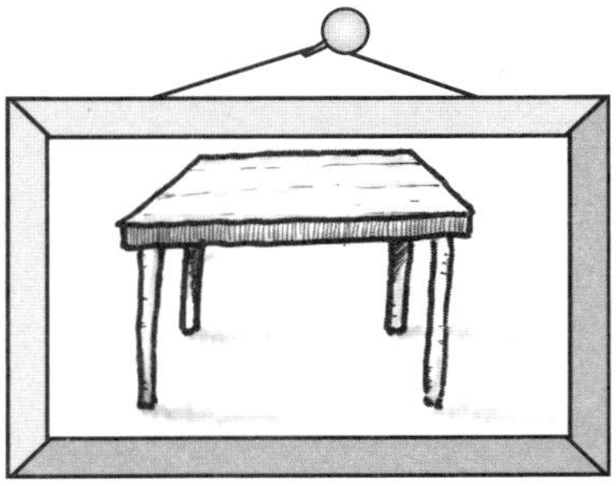

میز

meez

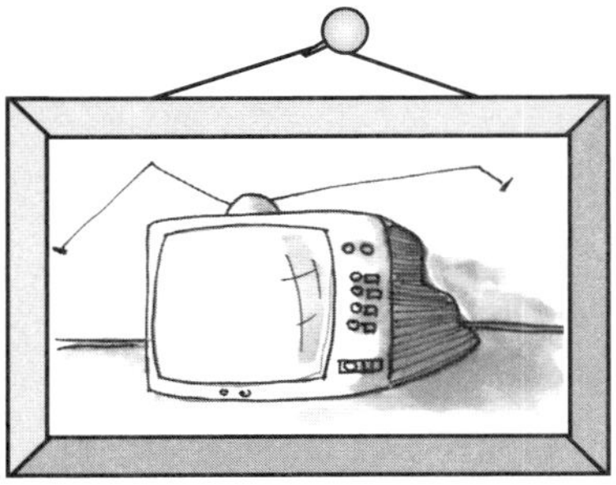

تِلویزیون

televeezyon

پَنجَره

panjareh

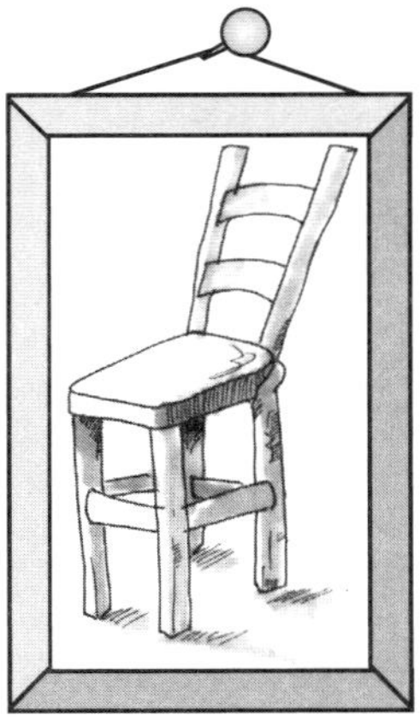

صَندَلی

sandalee

کامپیوتِر

kaampyooter

تِلِفُن

telefon

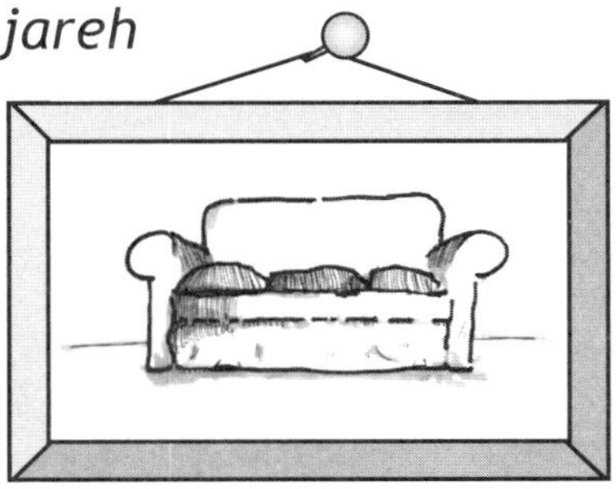

کاناپه *kaanaapeh*

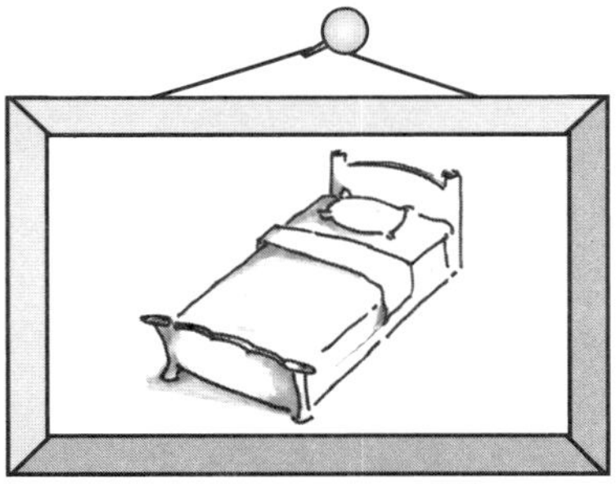

تَختِ خواب

takhteh khaab

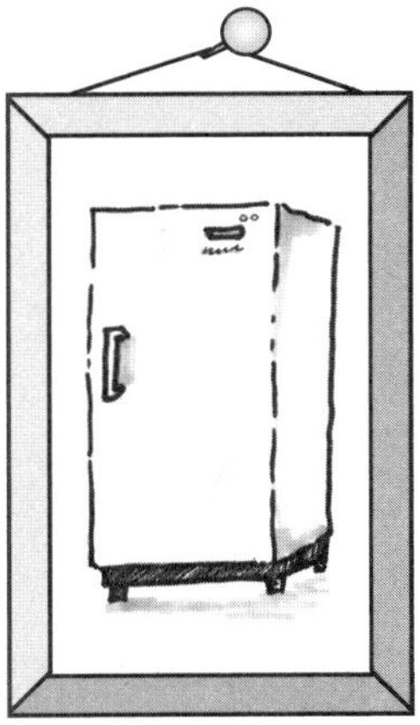

یَخچال

yakhchaal

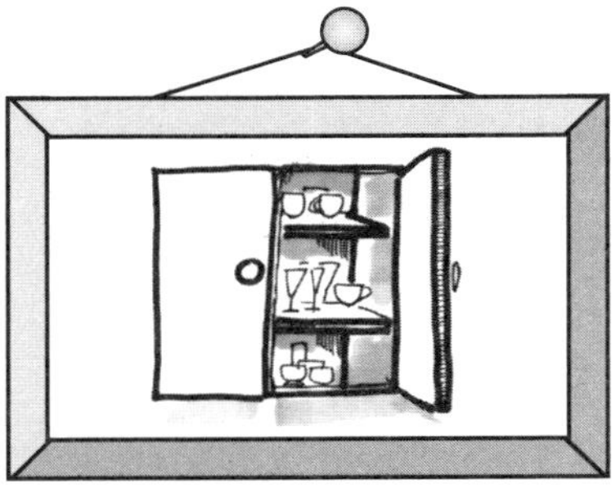

قَفَسه

ghafaseh

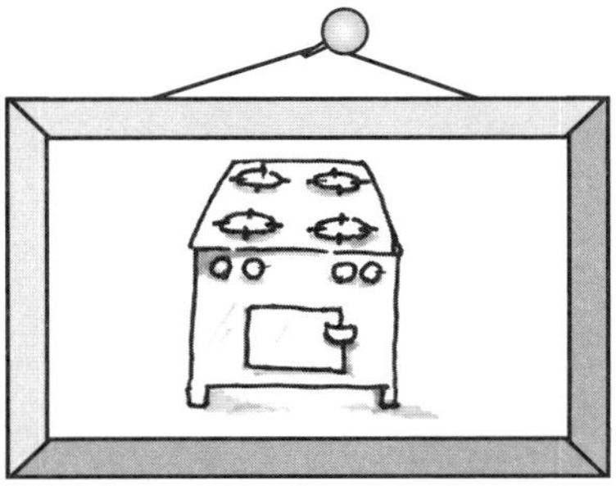

خوراکپَز

khoraakpaz

دَر

dar

Match the pictures with the words, as in the example.

کاناپه
تَختِ خواب
پَنجَره
میز
تِلویزیون
صَندَلی
کامپیوتِر
تِلُفن

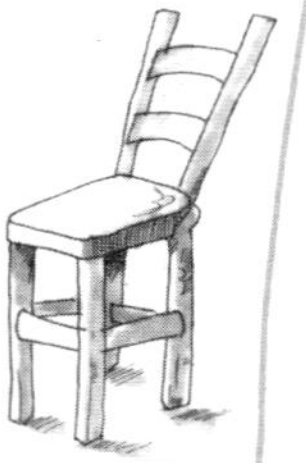

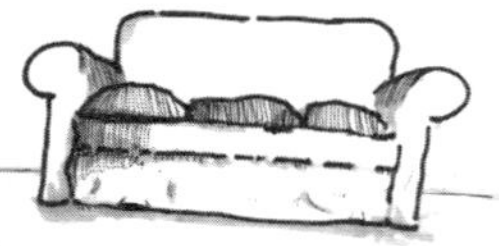
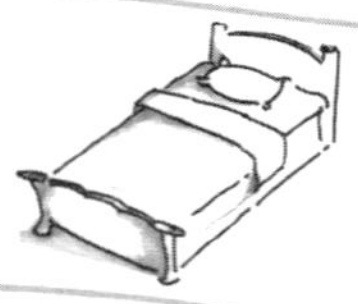
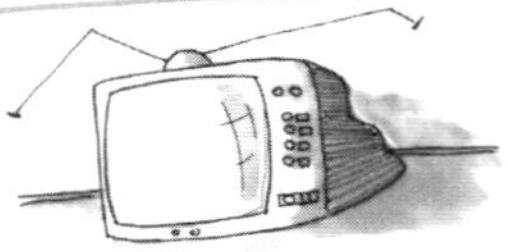

Now match the Persian household words to the English.

door
cupboard
stove
bed
table
chair
fridge
computer

تَختِ خواب
قَفَسه
صَندَلی
دَر
کامپیوتِر
یَخچال
میز
خوراکپَز

Match the words and their pronunciation.

میز

قَفَسه

کامپیوتِر

تَختِ خواب

پَنجَره

تِلِفُن

تِلِویزیون

صَندَلی

panjareh

takhteh khaab

telefon

sandalee

televeezyon

meez

kaampyooter

ghafaseh

See if you can find these words in the word square.

The words run *right to left*.

یَخچال

میز

صَندَلی

دَر

کاناپه

قَفَسه

ف	و	ـه	پـ	ـا	نـ	ـا	کـ
ط	ی	لـ	د	نـ	صـ	ا	فـ
د	هـ	تـ	ز	لـ	چـ	ر	د
ـه	بـ	ـه	سـ	فـ	قـ	و	ظ
ر	فـ	ی	لا	ـا	کـ	نـ	صـ
ن	یـ	ا	جـ	س	پـ	عـ	ط
ل	ـا	چـ	خـ	یـ	ذ	فـ	و
ث	ز	یـ	ـمـ	حـ	پ	ا	بـ

Decide where the household items should go. Then write the correct number in the picture, as in the example.

10 کامپیوتِر	7 قَفَسه	4 تِلویزیون	1 میز
11 پَنجَره	8 خوراکپَز	5 تِلفُن	2 صَندَلی
12 دَر	9 یَخچال	6 تَختِ خواب	3 کاناپه

Now see if you can fill in the household word at the bottom of the page by choosing the correct Persian.

	میز	c	صَندَلی	b	تِلِفُن	w
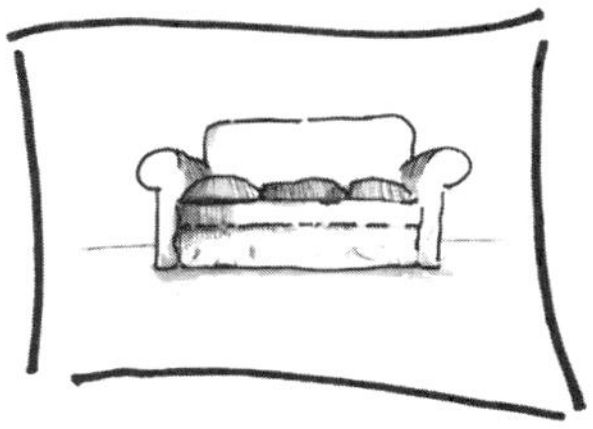	کاناپه	i	یَخچال	a	قَفَسه	f
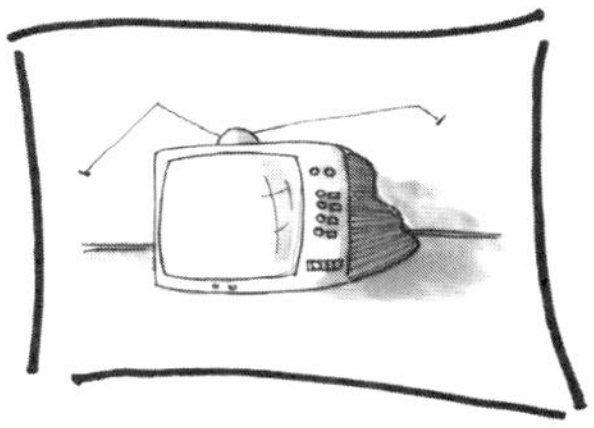	کامپیوتِر	d	تِلِویزیون	n	در	i
	صَندَلی	b	میز	d	یَخچال	k
	کاناپه	s	تِلِفُن	t	پَنجَره	o
	در	g	قَفَسه	w	صَندَلی	e

English word: (w) ( ) ( ) ( ) ( ) ( )

2 CLOTHES

Look at the pictures of different clothes.
Tear out the flashcards for this topic.
Follow steps 1 and 2 of the plan in the introduction.

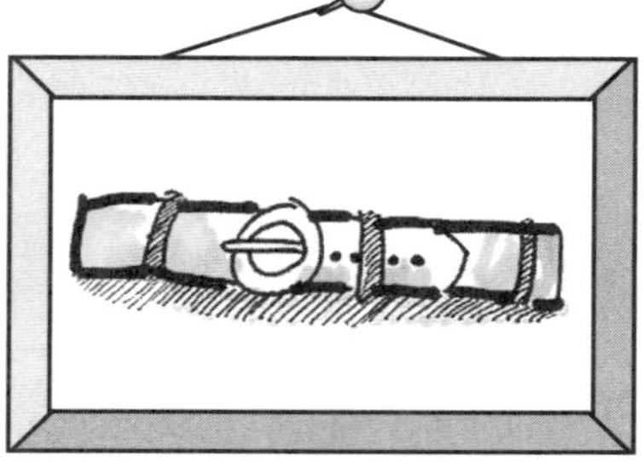

کَمَربَند

kamarband

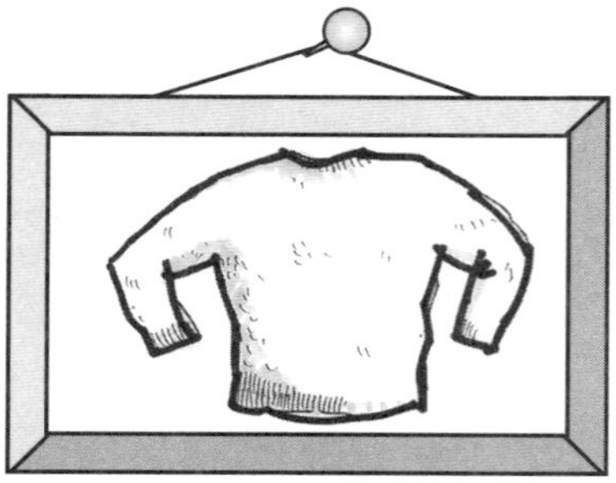

پوليوِر

poleever

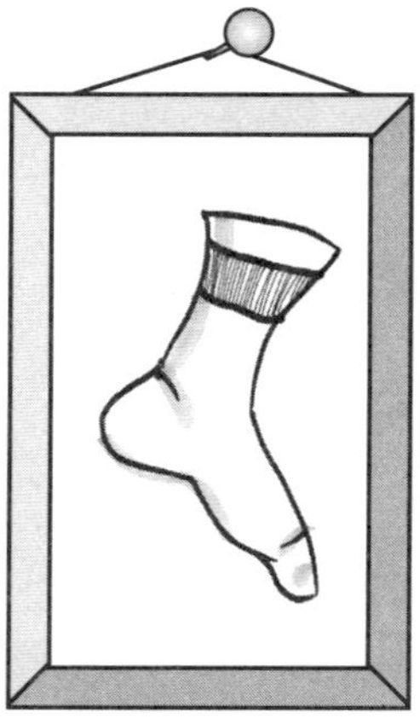

جوراب

jooraab

شورت

short

شَلوار

shalvaar

تی شِرت

tee shert

پالتو

paalto

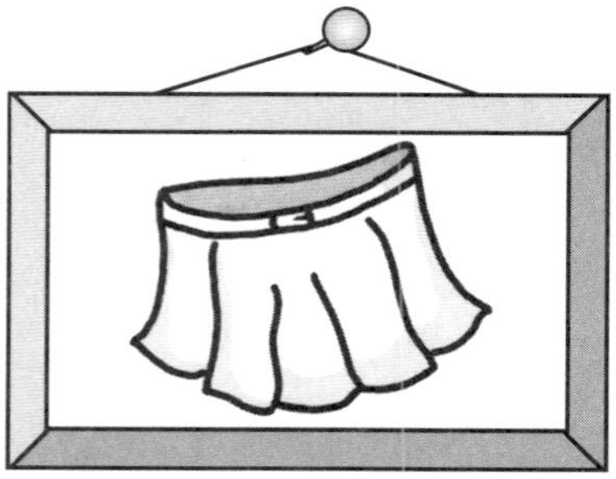

دامَن *daaman*

پيراهَنِ زنانه

peeraahaneh zanaaneh

کُلاه

kolaah

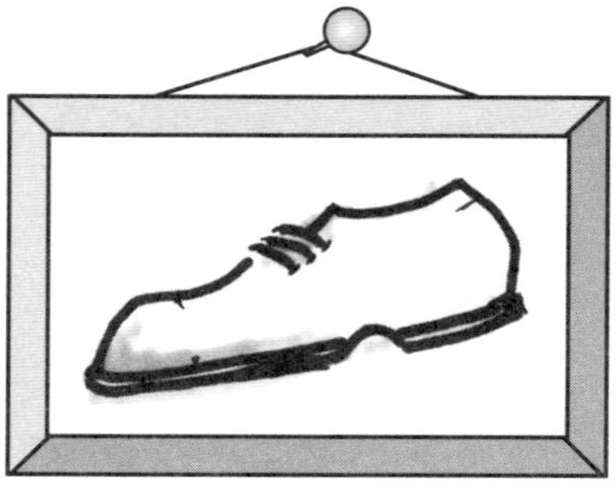

کَفش *kafsh*

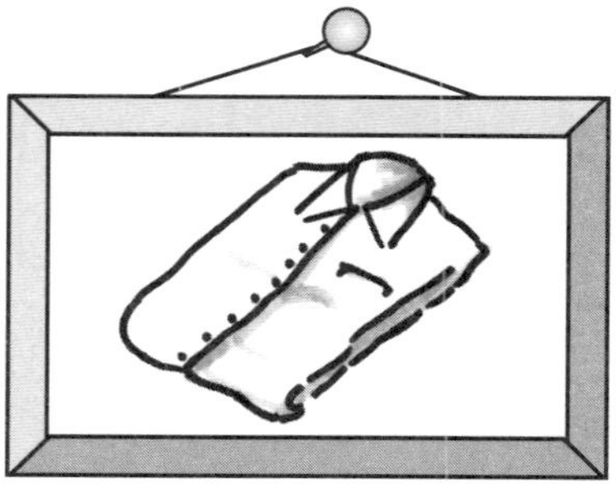

پيراهَنِ مَردانه

peeraahaneh mardaaneh

Match the Persian words and their pronunciation.

دامَن

شورت

کَفش

کَمَربَند

پالتو

تی شِرت

کُلاه

جوراب

daaman

tee shert

short

jooraab

kolaah

paalto

kamarband

kafsh

See if you can find these clothes in the word square.

The words run *right to left*.

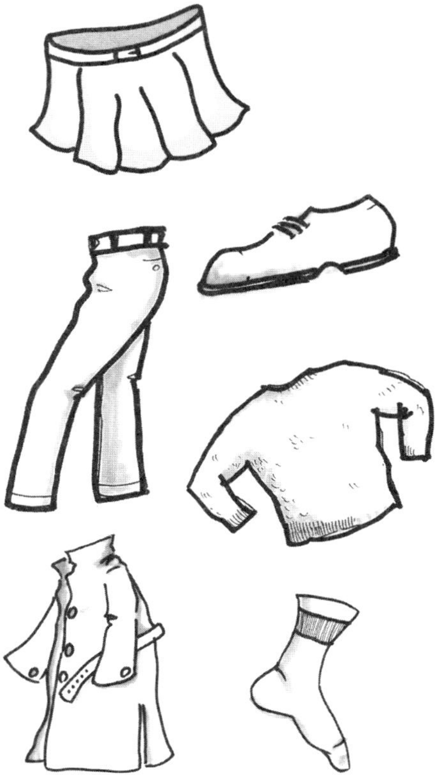

ر	فـ	پـ	لـ	بـ	ثـ	يـ	قـ
ط	ر	ا	و	لـ	شـ	قـ	کـ
د	هـ	تـ	ب	ا	ر	و	جـ
ن	مـ	ا	د	فـ	قـ	و	ظ
و	تـ	لـ	ا	پـ	چـ	يـ	مـ
ظ	يـ	ن	ش	فـ	ک	نـ	فـ
م	ر	و	يـ	لـ	و	پـ	و
ث	فـ	پ	غـ	چ	ا	ذ	حـ

Now match the Persian words, their pronunciation, and the English meaning, as in the example.

kafsh

sock

short

shorts

تی شِرت

belt

پالتو

paalto

شَلوار

tee shert

کَفش

shoe

جوراب

kolaah

کَمَربَند

t-shirt

coat

hat

کُلاه

jooraab

shalvaar

شورت

trousers

kamarband

Candy is going on vacation. Count how many of each type of clothing she is packing in her suitcase.

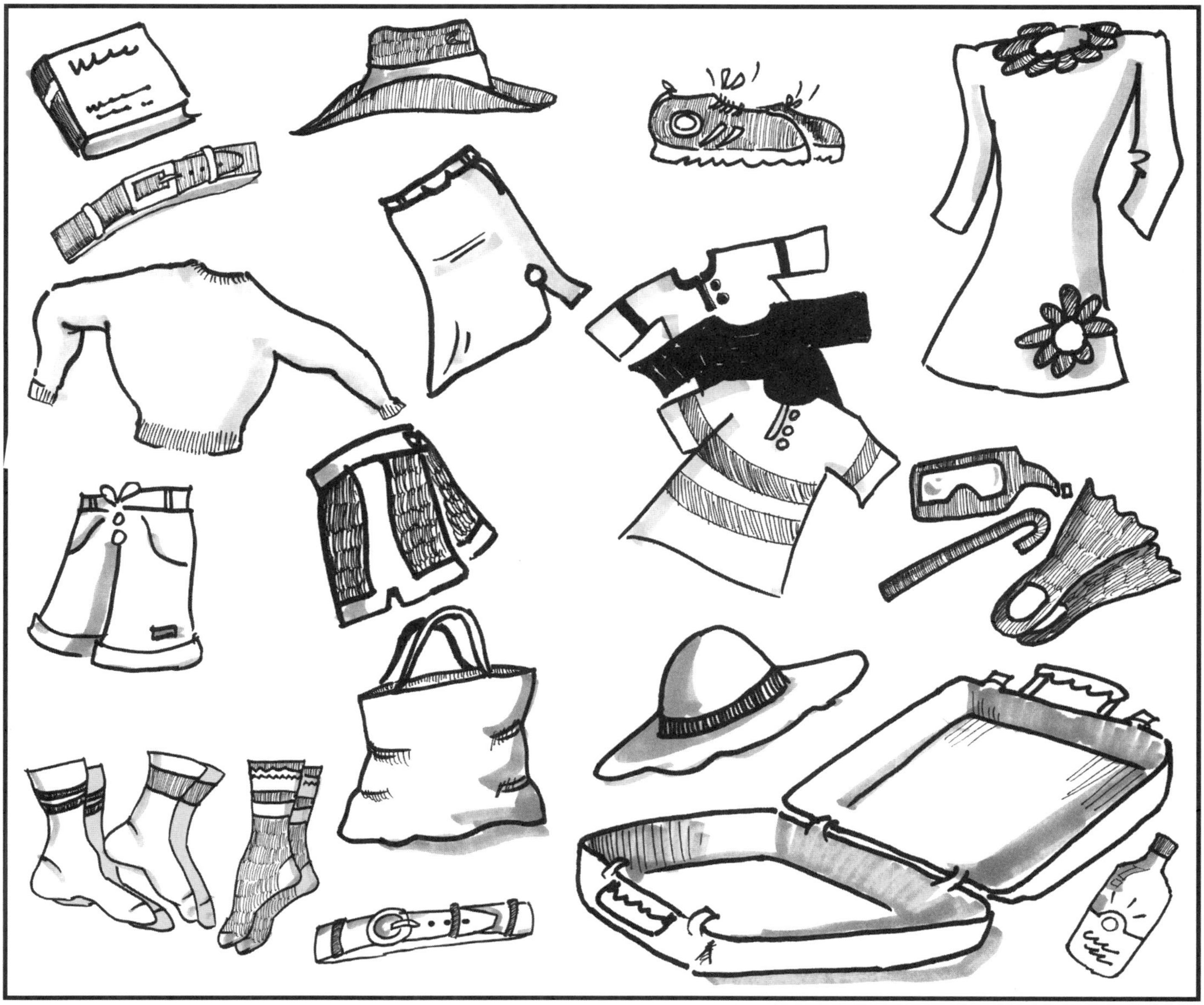

کُلاه	2	پالتو		کَمَربَند		کَفش	
شَلوار		شورت		پیراهَن زَنانه		جوراب	
دامَن		تی شِرت		پیراهَن مَردانه		پولیوِر	

Someone has ripped up the Persian words for clothes. Can you join the two halves of the words, as the example?

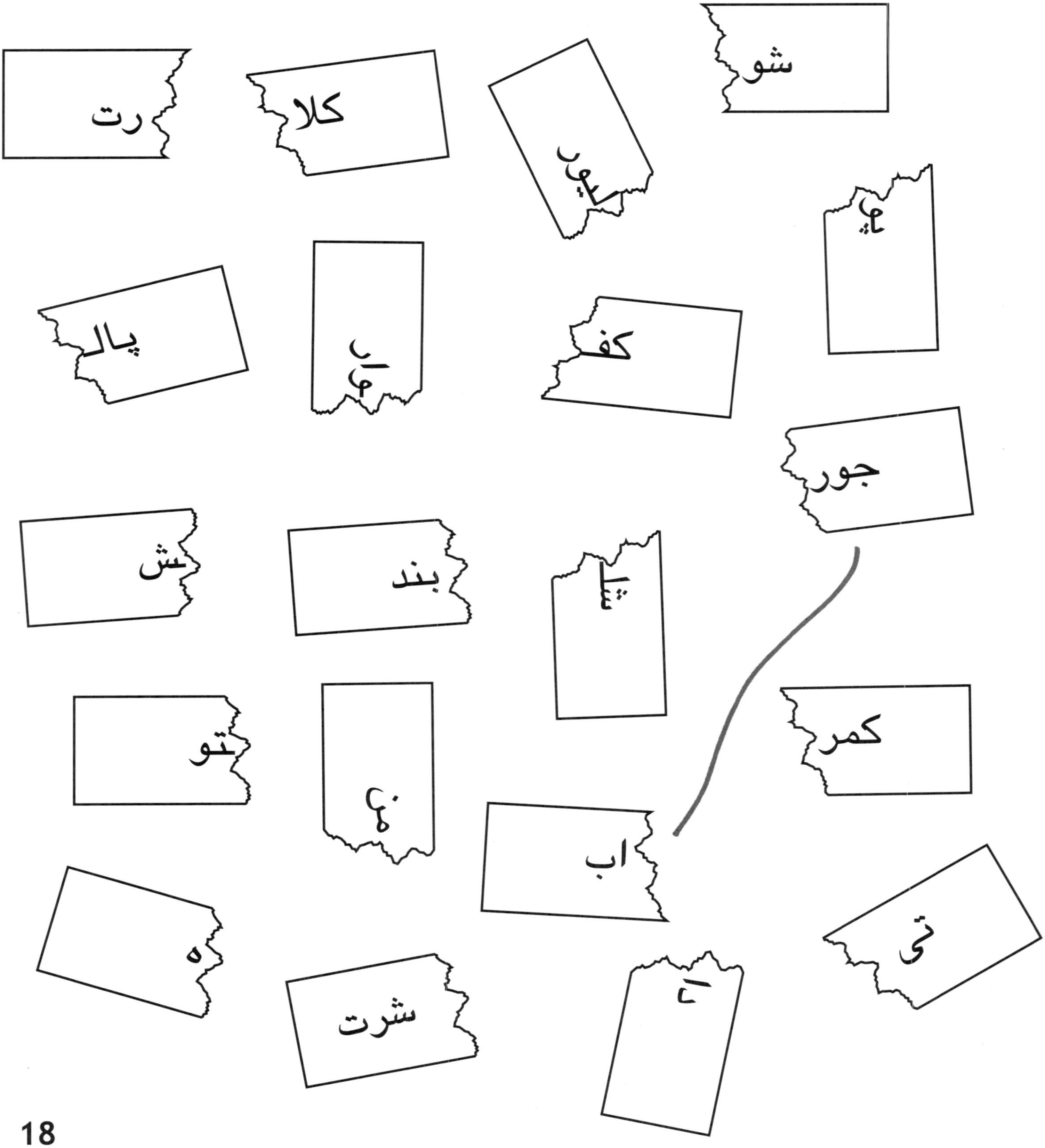

❸ Around town

Look at the pictures of things you might find around town.
Tear out the flashcards for this topic.
Follow steps 1 and 2 of the plan in the introduction.

هُتِل

hotel

اُتوبوس

otoboos

خانه

khaaneh

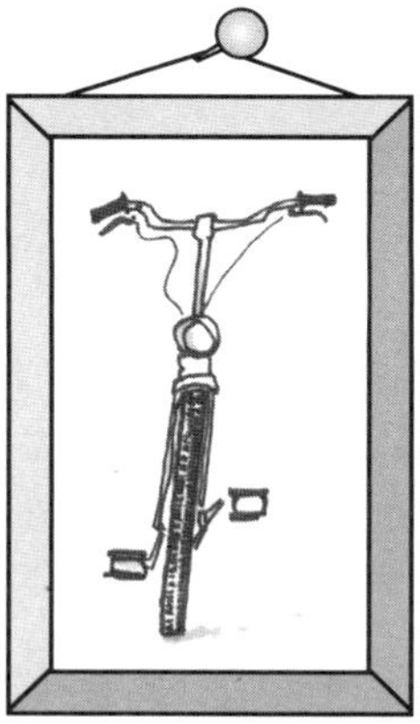

دوچَرخه

docharkheh

ماشین

maasheen

سینِما *seenemaa*

قَطار *ghataar*

تاکسی *taaksee*

مَدرِسه *madreseh*

جاده *jaaddeh*

فُروشگاه

forooshgaah

رِستوران

restooraan

Match the Persian words to their English equivalents.

cinema

shop —— فُروشگاه

hotel

taxi

car

train

school

house

هُتِل

ماشین

مَدرِسه

خانه

سینِما

قَطار

تاکسی

Now list the correct order of the English words to match the Persian word chain, as in the example.

تاکسی — قَطار — ماشین — دوچَرخه — جاده — خانه — اُتوبوس

bicycle	taxi	house	train	bus	road	car
4	____	____	____	____	____	____

Match the words to the signs.

مَدِرسه ماشین دوچَرخه اُتوبوس

رِستوران قَطار هُتِل تاکسی

Now choose the Persian word that matches the picture to fill in the English word at the bottom of the page.

تاکسی (c) | جاده (f) | خانه (s)

جاده (c) | ماشین (a) | اُتوبوس (k)

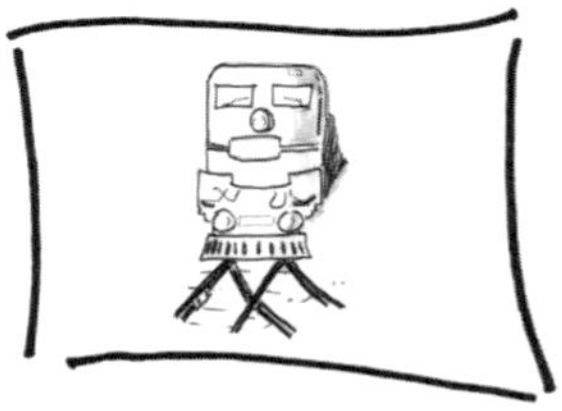

قَطار (h) | مَدرِسه (e) | رِستوران (u)

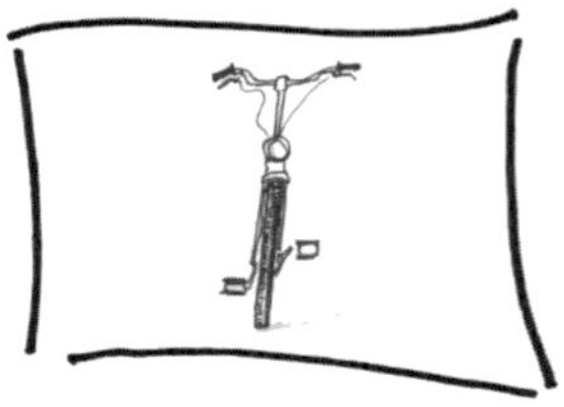

ماشین (b) | دوچَرخه (o) | قَطار (w)

مَدرِسه (o) | جاده (h) | هُتِل (s)

تاکسی (r) | خانه (g) | سینِما (l)

English word: (s) ( ) ( ) ( ) ( ) ( )

Now match the Persian to the pronunciation.

اُتوبوس

تاکسی

مَدرِسه

ماشین

هُتِل

خانه

دوچَرخه

قَطار

فُروشگاه

سینِما

رستوران

جاده

khaaneh

otoboos

ghataar

restooraan

forooshgaah

madreseh

taaksee

seenemaa

jaaddeh

hotel

maasheen

docharkheh

❹ COUNTRYSIDE

Look at the pictures of things you might find in the countryside.
Tear out the flashcards for this topic.
Follow steps 1 and 2 of the plan in the introduction.

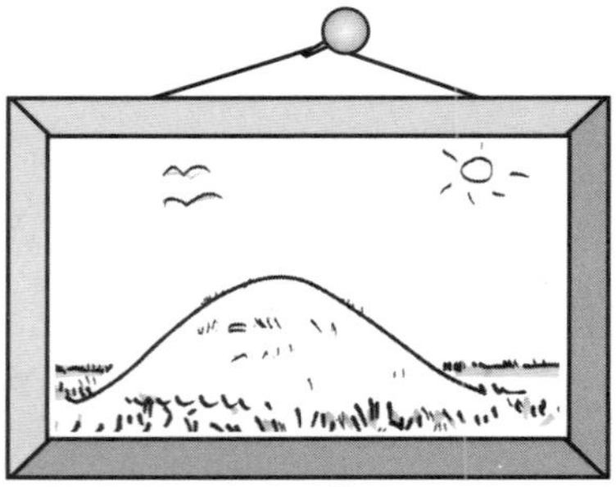

تَپه *tappeh*

پُل *pol*

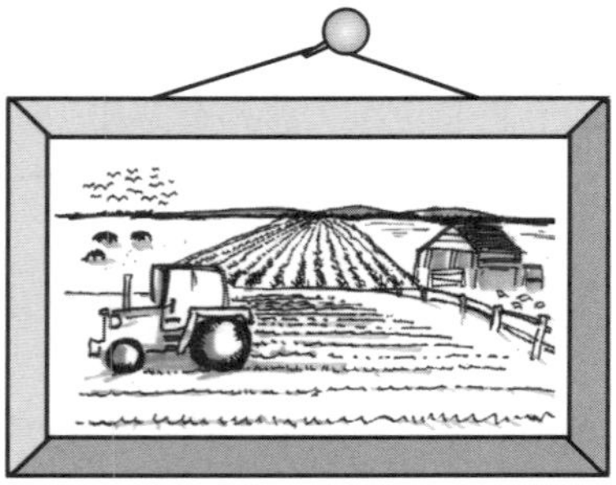

مَزرَعه

mazra'eh

کوه

kooh

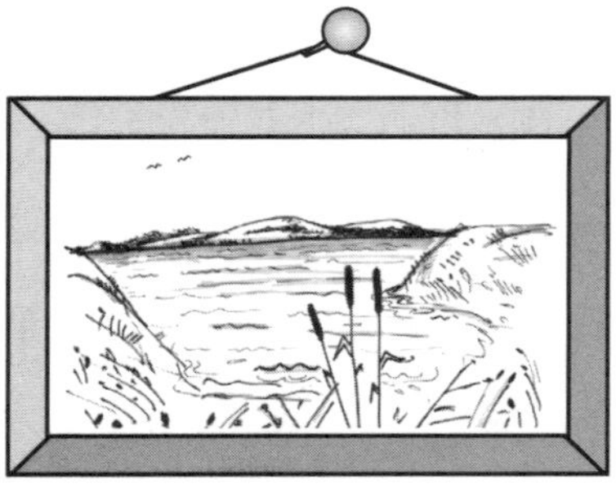

دَریاچه

daryaacheh

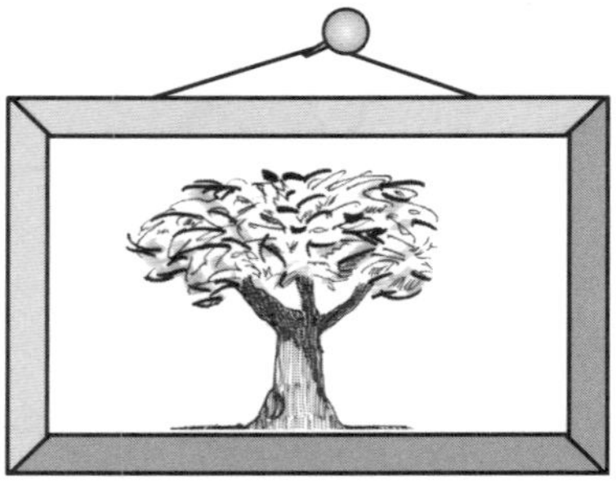

دِرَخت

derakht

گل

gol

رود *rood*

دَریا *daryaa*

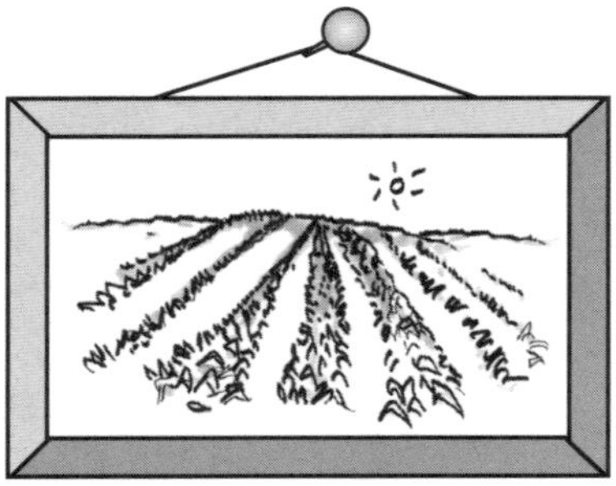

کِشتزار *keshtzaar*

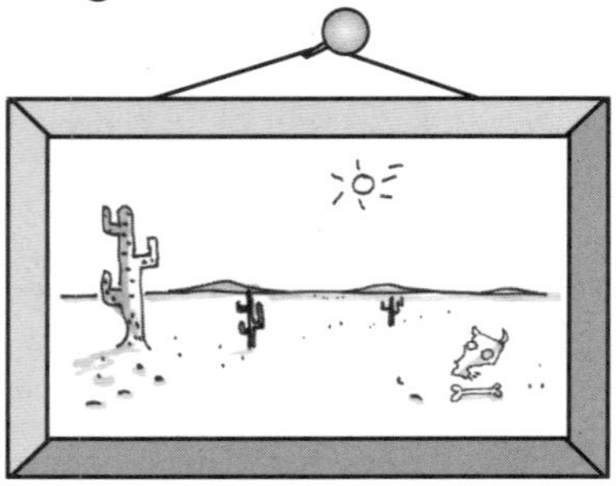

بیابان *biaabaan*

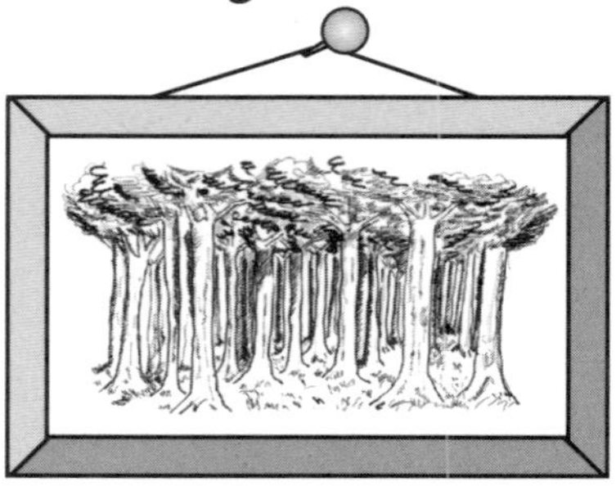

جَنگل

jangal

Can you match all the countryside words to the pictures?

کوه

مَزرَعه

دَریا

جَنگل

بیابان

تَپه

دَریاچه

پُل

رود

گل

دِرَخت

کِشتزار

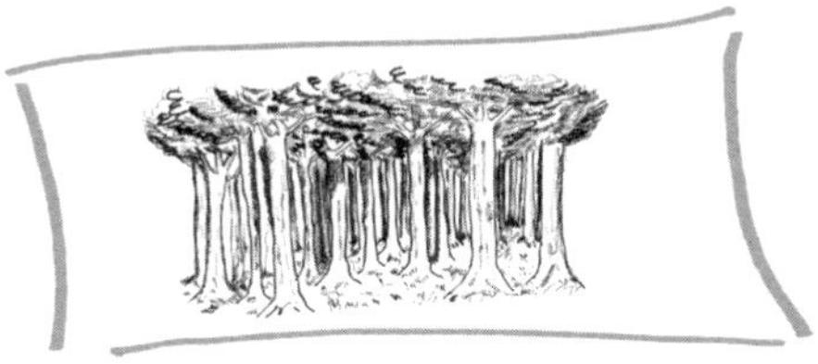

Now tick (✔) the features you can find in this landscape.

☐ تَپه	☐ بیابان	☐ دِرَخت	✔ پُل
☐ جَنگل	☐ کِشتزار	☐ دَریا	☐ کوه
☐ مَزرَعه	☐ گل	☐ رود	☐ دَریاچه

Match the Persian words and their pronunciation.

کوه

رود

جَنگل

بیابان

دَریا

مَزرَعه

پُل

کِشتزار

biaabaan

mazra`eh

keshtzaar

jangal

rood

pol

daryaa

kooh

See if you can find these words in the word square.

The words run *right to left*.

درخت

مزرعه

تپه

گل

پل

دریاچه

ک	و	ل	پـ	چـ	ـا	ر	د
ط	ی	ـه	پـ	تـ	صـ	ا	فـ
د	ـهـ	تـ	ز	ـلـ	چـ	ر	د
ـه	بـ	ت	خـ	ر	د	و	گـ
ک	فـ	ی	لا	ـا	کـ	نـ	صـ
پ	ـه	چـ	ـا	یـ	ر	د	ط
ل	گـ	چـ	خـ	یـ	ذ	فـ	و
ف	ز	ـه	عـ	ر	ز	مـ	بـ

Finally, test yourself by joining the Persian words, their pronunciation, and the English meanings, as in the example.

gol

lake

mazra`eh

کِشتزار

desert

mountain

رود

daryaacheh

مَزرَعه

keshtzaar

دَریاچه

farm

گل

daryaa

کوه

field

river

sea

دَریا

kooh

rood

بیابان

flower

biaabaan

5 OPPOSITES

Look at the pictures.
Tear out the flashcards for this topic.
Follow steps 1 and 2 of the plan in the introduction.

کَثیف
kaseef

تَمیز
tameez

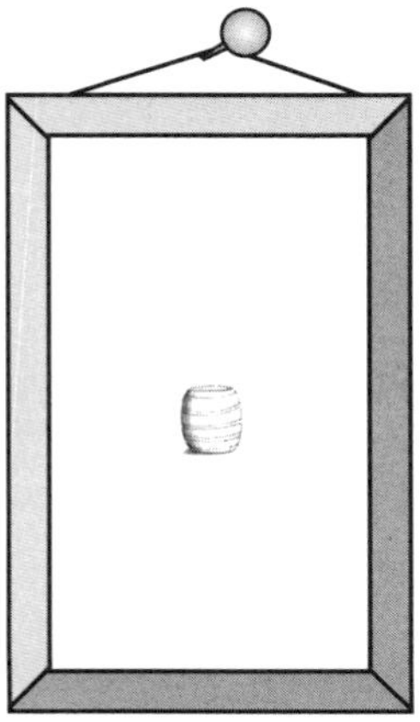

کوچِک
koochek

بُزُرگ
bozorg

اَرزان *arzaan*

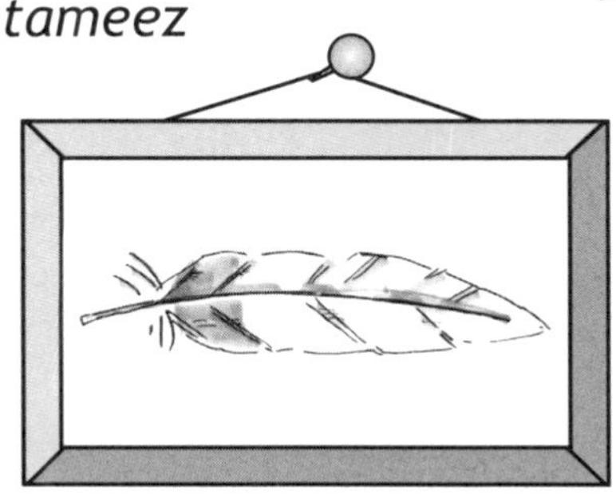

سَبُک *sabok*

آهِسته *aahesteh*

گِران *geraan*

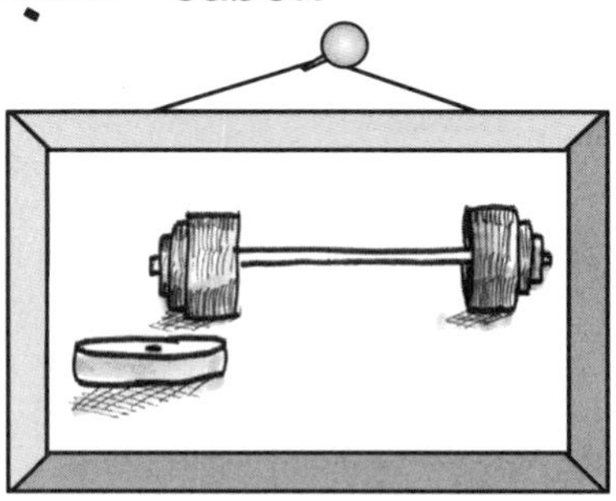

سَنگین *sangeen*

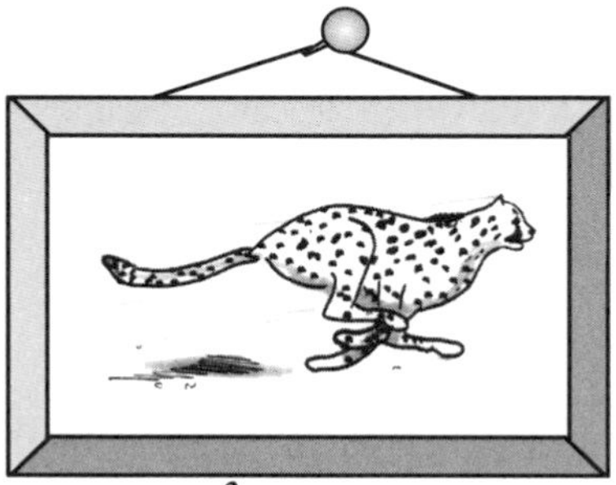

تُند *tond*

قَدیمی *ghadeemee*

جَدید *jadeed*

Join the Persian words to their English equivalents.

expensive	تَمیز
big	سَنگین
light	کوچک
slow	قَدیمی
clean	جَدید
cheap	اَرزان
dirty	تُند
small	آهِسته
heavy	گِران
new	کَثیف
fast	سَبُک
old	بُزُرگ

Now choose the Persian word that matches the picture to fill in the English word at the bottom of the page.

	تُند	c	آهِسته	t	تَمیز	h
	جَدید	d	اَرزان	a	کَثیف	h
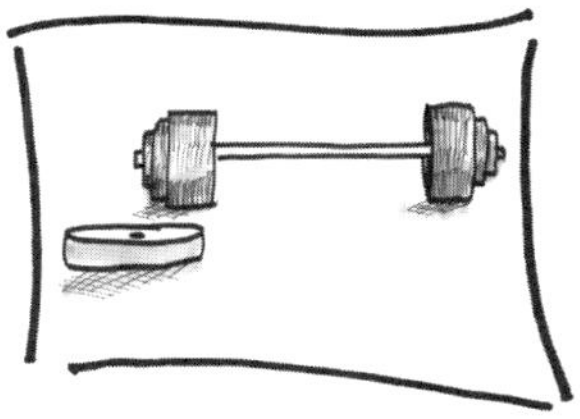	بُزُرگ	r	سَنگین	a	کوچک	u
	گِران	p	اَرزان	n	جَدید	o
	جَدید	g	سَبُک	c	کوچک	s
	تَمیز	m	قَدیمی	n	آهِسته	e

English word: ○ ○ ○ ○ ○ ○

Find the odd one out in these groups of words.

سَنگین	گِران	اَرزان

سَنگین	کوچک	سَبُک

جَدید	تُند	آهِسته

جَدید	قَدیمی	کَثیف

آهِسته	کَثیف	تَمیز

کوچک	بُزُرگ	اَرزان

Finally, join the English words to their Persian opposites, as in the example.

slow

heavy

قدیمی

small

بُزُرگ

جَدید

light

آهِسته

expensive

dirty

کَثیف

new

clean

fast

کوچک

سَنگین

تُند

big

گِران

old

تمیز

اَرزان

cheap

سَبُک

6 ANIMALS

Look at the pictures.
Tear out the flashcards for this topic.
Follow steps 1 and 2 of the plan in the introduction.

مُرغابی *morghaabee*

فیل

feel

گربه *gorbeh*

سَگ

sag

خَرگوش

khargoosh

میمون

meimoon

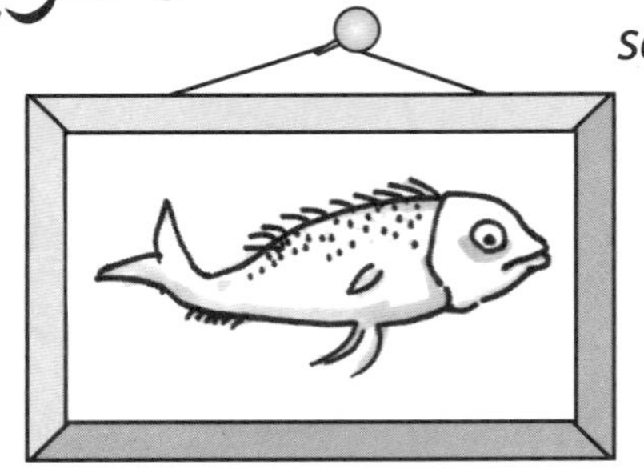

ماهی *maahee*

گوسفَند *goosfand*

موش *moosh*

گاو

gaav

اَسب *asb*

شیر *sheer*

Match the animals to their associated pictures, as in the example.

خَرگوش

اَسب

مِیمون

گُربه

گوسفَند

موش

سَگ

شیر

ماهی

گاو

Now match the Persian to the pronunciation.

خَرگوش

اَسب

مِیمون

سَگ

گُربه

موش

مُرغابی

ماهی

شیر

گوسفَند

فیل

گاو

morghaabee

gaav

maahee

khargoosh

sheer

sag

feel

goosfand

asb

gorbeh

moosh

meimoon

Tick (✔) the animal words you can find in the word pile.

قَطار
پَنجَره
گُربه
رود

قَفَسه
گوسفَند
فیل
خَرگوش

کَفش
سینِما
میز
کَثیف

ماهی
گاو
شیر
تَپه

Join the Persian animals to their English equivalents.

monkey	سَگ
cow	شیر
mouse	مِیمون
dog	فیل
sheep	خَرگوش
fish	ماهی
lion	موش
elephant	مُرغابی
cat	گاو
duck	گوسفَند
rabbit	اَسب
horse	گُربه

7 PARTS OF THE BODY

Look at the pictures of parts of the body.
Tear out the flashcards for this topic.
Follow steps 1 and 2 of the plan in the introduction.

اَنگُشت

angosht

سَر

sar

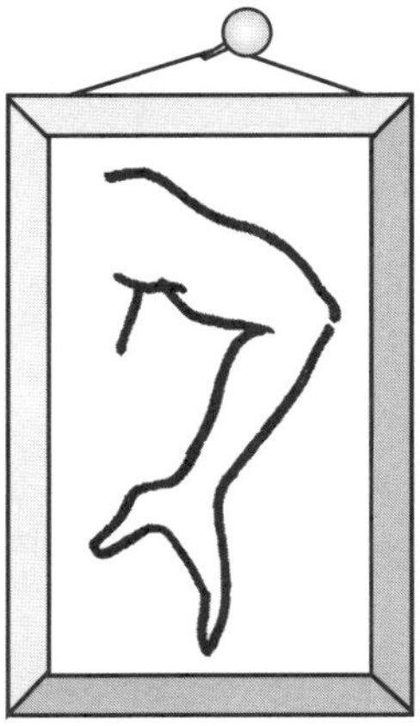

بـازو

baazoo

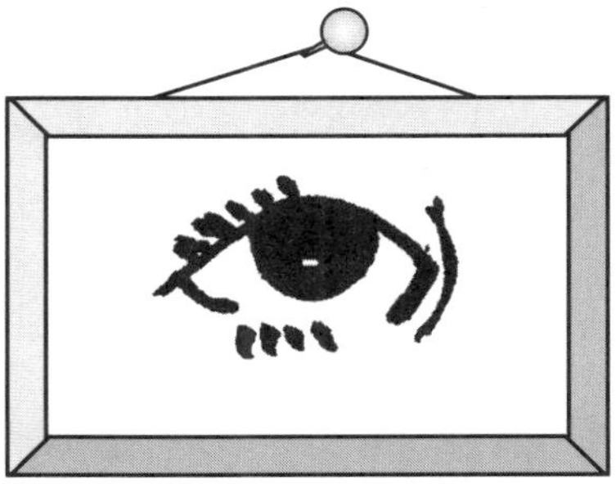

چِشم *cheshm*

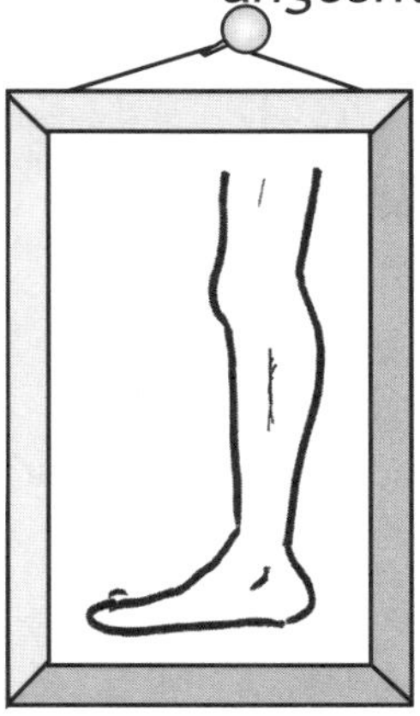

پـا *paa*

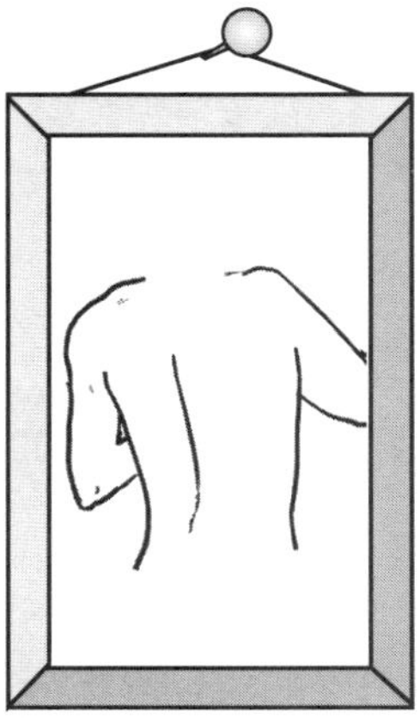

پُشت

posht

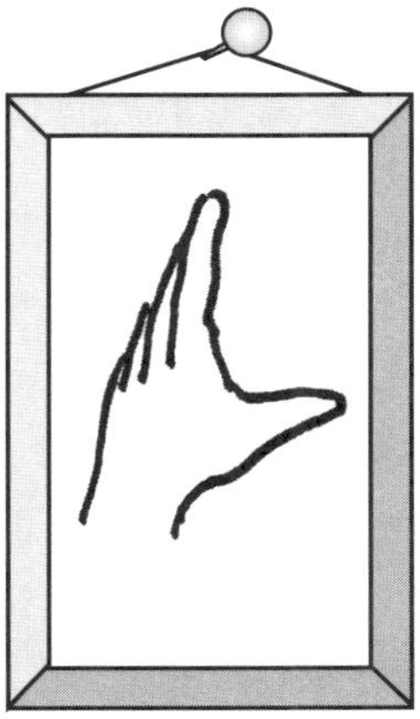

دَست

dast

مو *moo*

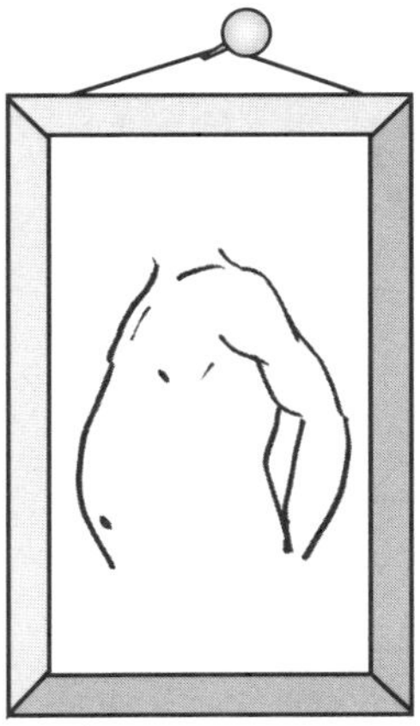

مِعده

me`deh

گوش *goosh*

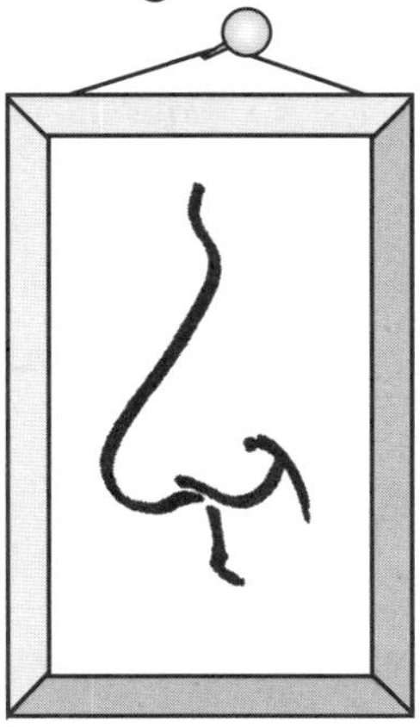

بینی *beenee*

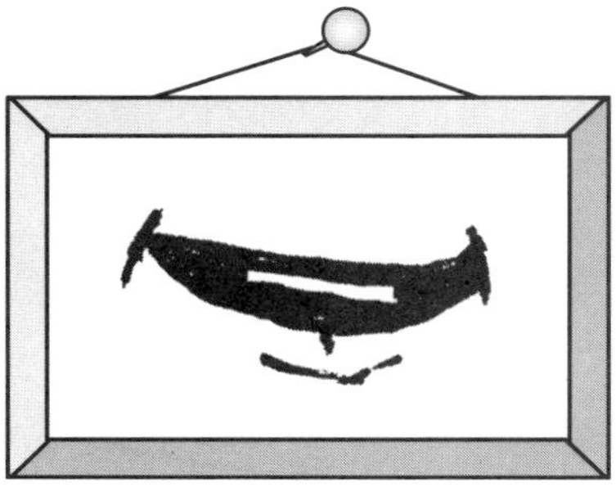

دَهـان *dahaan*

Someone has ripped up the Persian words for parts of the body. Can you join the two halves of the word again?

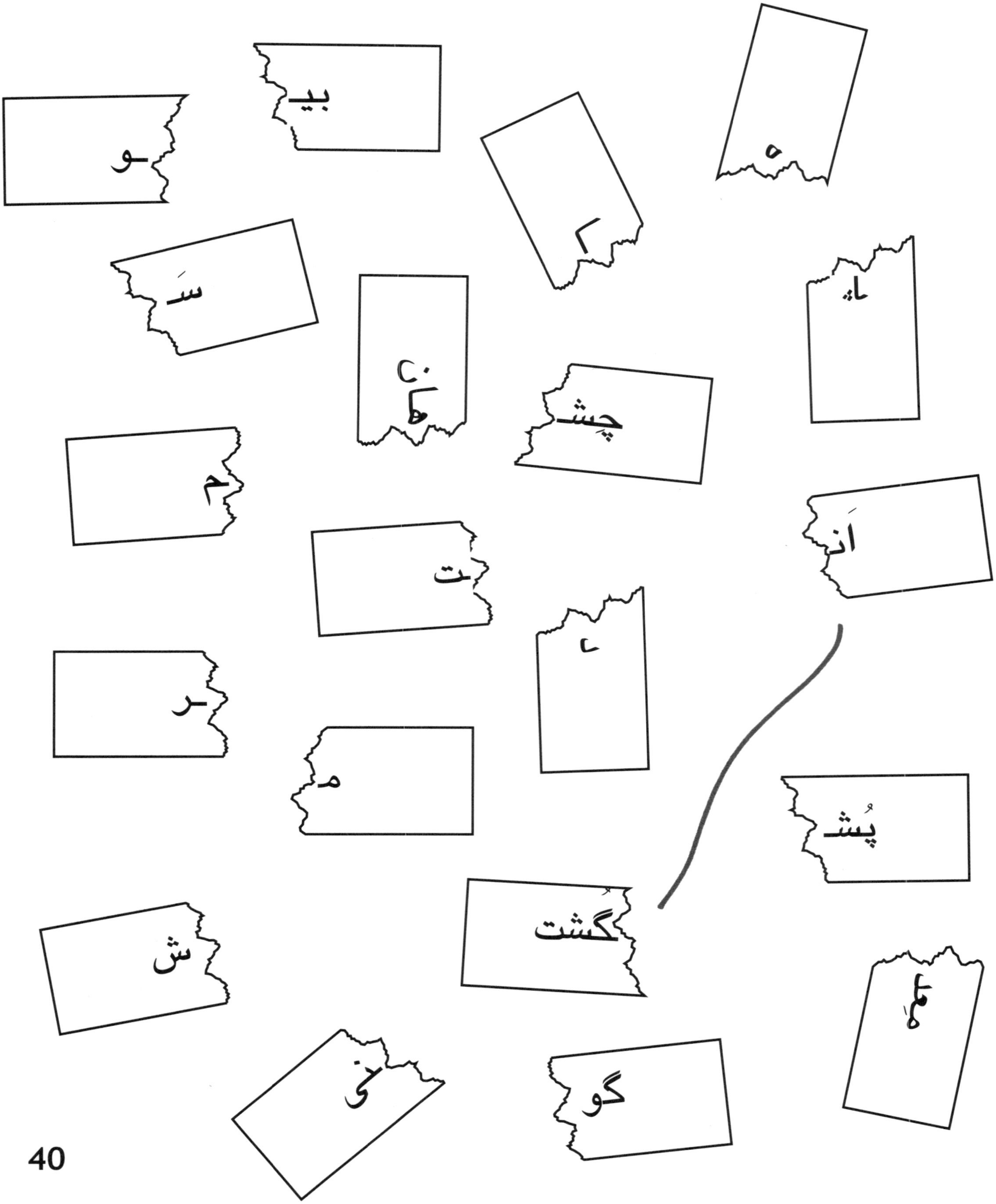

See if you can find and circle six parts of the body in the word square, then draw them in the boxes below.

The words run *right to left*.

ک	و	ل	شـ	ن	ا	هـ	د
ط	ی	ـه	پـ	تـ	ـصـ	ا	فـ
و	ـمـ	ی	ز	یـ	بـ	ر	د
ـه	بـ	ت	خـ	ـا	پـ	و	گ
ی	ـنـ	یـ	بـ	ـا	ک	نـ	صـ
پ	ـه	ش	و	گ	ر	د	گ
م	شـ	چ	خـ	یـ	ذ	ک	و
ف	ز	ـه	عـ	ر	ز	مـ	بـ

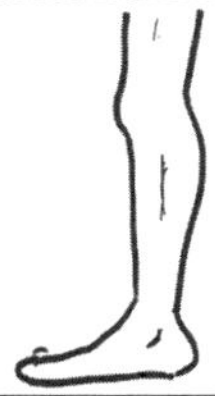

سَر

گوش

مِعده

بینی

بـازو

دَهـان

چِشم

پُشت

baazoo

beenee

posht

sar

me`deh

goosh

cheshm

dahaan

Label the body with the correct number, and write the pronunciation next to the words.

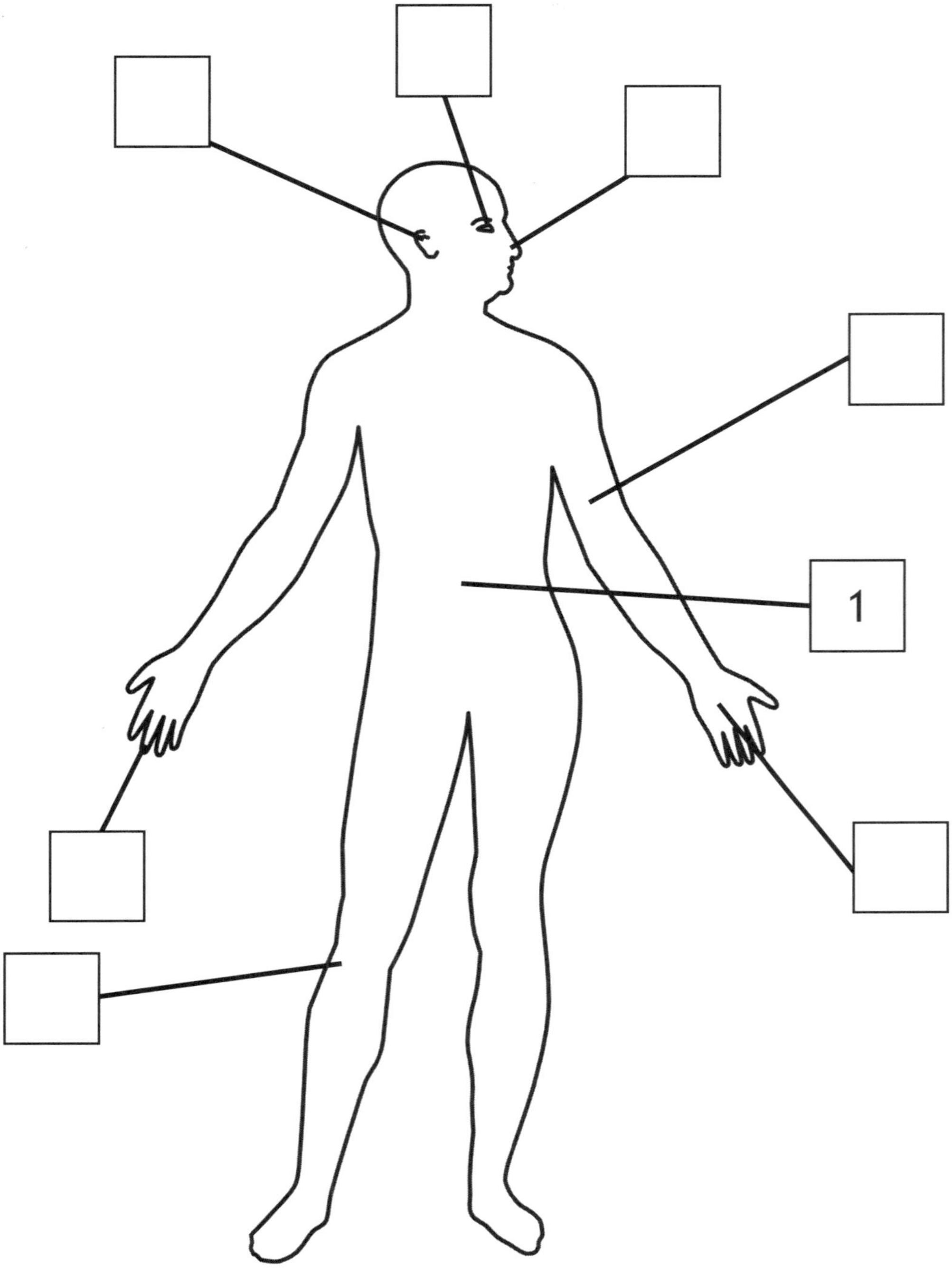

1	مِعده	me`deh	5	بازو	....
2	بینی	....	6	دَست	....
3	گوش	....	7	پا	....
4	چِشم	....	8	اَنگشت	....

Finally, match the Persian words, their pronunciation, and the English meanings, as in the example.

angosht

hair

paa

stomach

پُشت

hand

بازو

baazoo

مو

dast

مِعده

back

انگُشت

goosh

دَست

arm

finger

ear — گوش

posht

moo

پا

me`deh

leg

8 USEFUL EXPRESSIONS

Look at the pictures.
Tear out the flashcards for this topic.
Follow steps 1 and 2 of the plan in the introduction.

کُجا؟ *kojaa?*

نه *na*

بَله *baleh*

خُدا حافِظ

khodaa haafez

سَلام *salaam*

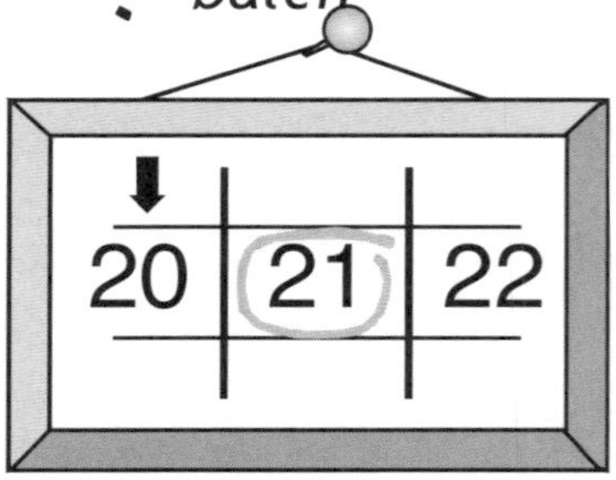

دیروز *deerooz*

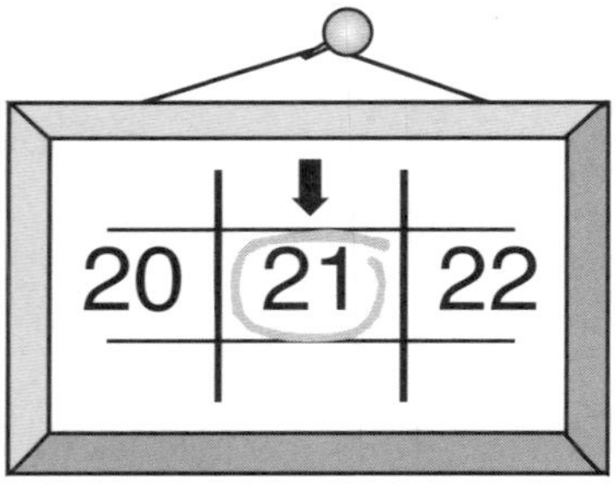

اِمروز *emrooz*

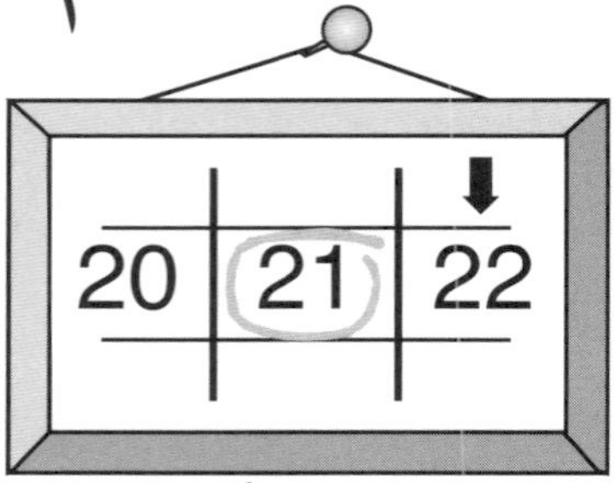

فَردا *fardaa*

اینجا

eenjaa

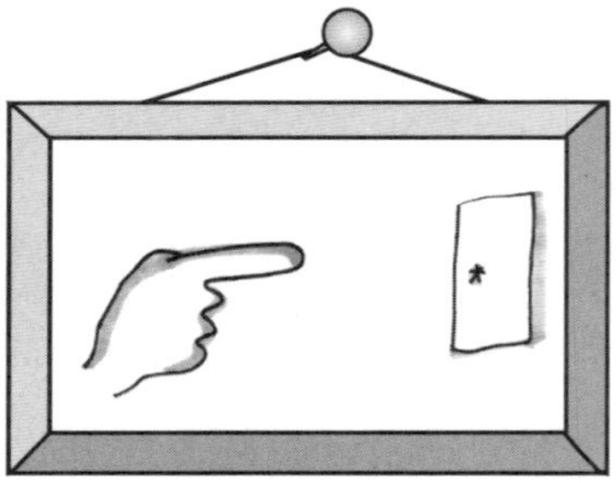

آنجا *aanjaa*

حالا *haalaa*

چَند؟ *chand?*

بِبَخشید

bebakhsheed

عالی! *aalee!*

لُطفاً

lotfan

مَمنون *mamnoon*

Match the Persian words to their English equivalents.

great!	دیروز
yes	بَله
yesterday	اینجا
where?	عالی!
today	لُطفاً
here	نه
please	اِمروز
no	کُجا؟

Now match the Persian to the pronunciation.

Persian	Pronunciation
آنجا	*khodaa haafez*
سَلام	*salaam*
فَردا	*aalee!*
خُدا حافِظ	*mamnoon*
چَند؟	*fardaa*
مَمنون	*bebakhsheed*
بِبَخشید	*chand?*
عالی!	*aanjaa*

Choose the Persian word that matches the picture to fill in the English word at the bottom of the page.

	اینجا	p	نه	c	بَله	t
	مَمنون	j	حالا	a	لُطفاً	l
	بَله	m	نه	e	اِمروز	i
	آنجا	b	سَلام	a	حالا	x
	کُجا؟	s	عالی!	h	چَند؟	t
	دیروز	b	نه	y	بَله	e

English word: (p) ( ) ( ) ( ) ( ) ( )

What are these people saying? Write the correct number in each speech bubble, as in the example.

1 سَلام
2 لُطفاً
3 بَله
4 نه
5 اینجا
6 بِبَخشید
7 کُجا؟
8 چَند؟

Finally, match the Persian words, their pronunciation, and the English meanings, as in the example.

mamnoon

hello

bebakh-sheed

please

آنجا

thank you

سَلام

aanjaa

فَردا

fardaa

نه

sorry

بِبَخشید

baleh

لُطفاً

no

there

yes

بَله

salaam

lotfan

مَمنون

tomorrow

na

ROUND-UP

This section is designed to review all the 100 words you have met in the different topics. It is a good idea to test yourself with your flashcards before trying this section.

These ten objects are hidden in the picture. Can you find and circle them?

ماهی   دوچرخه   کلاه   در   صندلی

گل   پالتو   جوراب   تخت خواب   سگ

See if you can remember all these words.

امروز

اتوبوس

تند

بینی

بیابان

بله

قفسه

شیر

پیراهن زنانه

ارزان

رود

پا

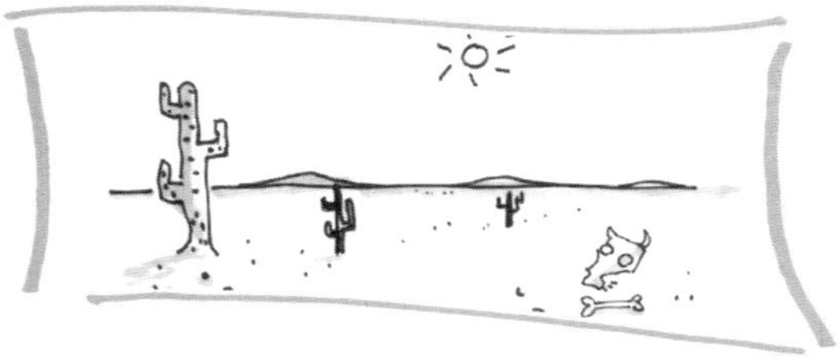

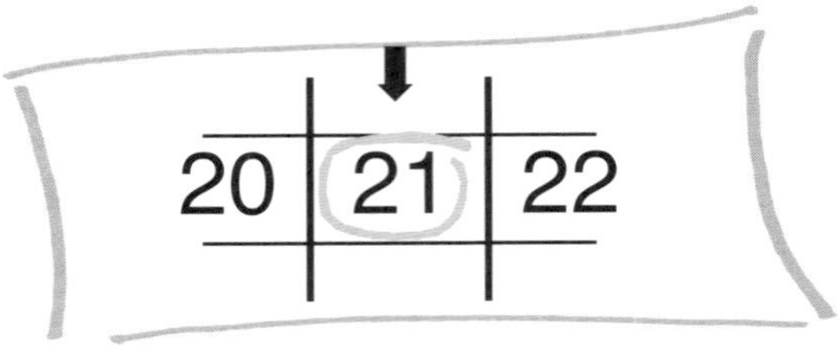

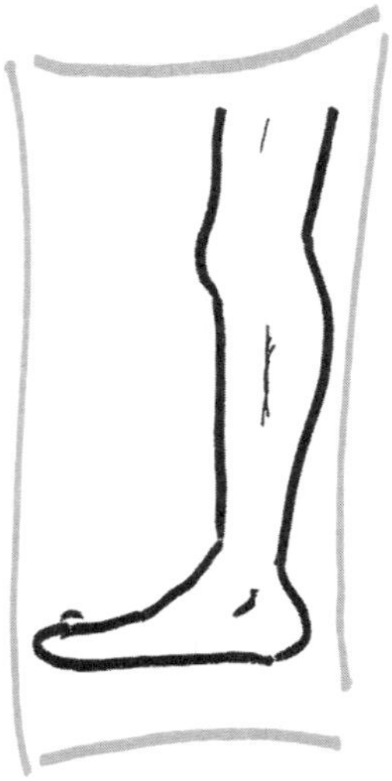

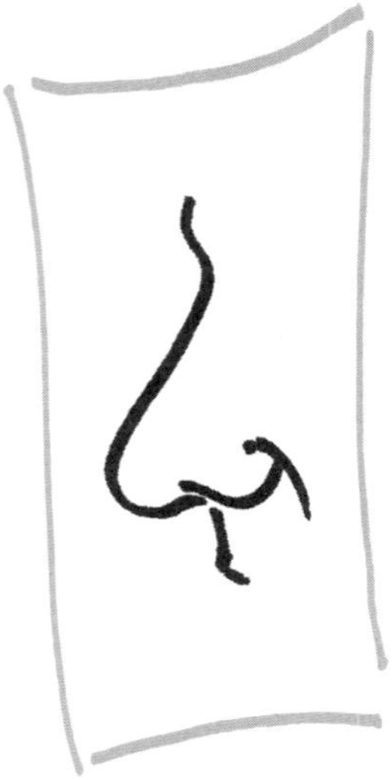

Find the odd one out in these groups of words and say why.

سگ	گاو	میز	میمون

Because it isn't an animal.

ماشین	اتوبوس	قطار	تلفن
کشتزار	پالتو	شورت	دامن
دریا	دریاچه	رود	درخت
سنگین	کثیف	تمیز	سینما
خرگوش	گربه	ماهی	شیر
بازو	کاناپه	سر	معده
لطفاً	دیروز	امروز	فردا
خوراکپز	تختخواب	قفسه	یخچال

Look at the objects below for 30 seconds.

Cover the picture and try to remember all the objects.

Circle the Persian words for those you remember.

گل

کفش

ممنون

در

ماشین

نه

اینجا

پالتو

قطار

کمربند

کوه

صندلی

اسب

جوراب

تی شرت

چشم

تخت خواب

شورت

تاکسی

تلویزیون

میمون

Now match the Persian words, their pronunciation, and the English meanings, as in the example.

mamnoon

lake

khaaneh

خانه

bed

thank you

کجا؟

sangeen

جنگل

kojaa?

سنگین

where?

دریاچه

poleever

تخت خواب

house

forest

sweater

پولیور

daryaacheh

takhteh khaab

ممنون

heavy

jangal

Fill in the English phrase at the bottom of the page.

	کاناپه	w	تاکسی	g	بینی	t
	پالتو	o	کثیف	a	پل	e
	کجا؟	m	چند؟	l	اینجا	i
	گاو	b	پنجره	l	رستوران	h
	اسب	e	چشم	a	سگ	d
	چشم	o	میز	p	بله	v
	تپه	n	نه	y	در	r
	خرگوش	n	جاده	e	خوراکپز	s

English phrase: (w) ( ) ( ) ( )   ( ) ( ) ( ) ( ) !

Look at the two pictures and tick (✔) the objects that are different in Picture B.

Picture A

Picture B

شورت	☐
تی شرت	☐
در	☐
گربه	☐
صندلی	☐
ماهی	☐
جوراب	☐
سگ	☐

Now join the Persian words to their English equivalents.

fridge	بازو
trousers	معده
shop	کوچک
school	یخچال
river	فروشگاه
great!	عالی!
small	رود
light	شلوار
arm	تمیز
stomach	سبک
clean	اسب
horse	مدرسه

Try to match the Persian to the pronunciation.

سلام	seenemaa
دیروز	khoraakpaz
خوراکپز	goosfand
سینما	keshtzaar
تاکسی	angosht
کوه	salaam
کشتزار	feel
بزرگ	taaksee
جدید	bozorg
گوسفند	jadeed
انگشت	kooh
فیل	deerooz

Snake game.

- You will need a die and counter(s). You can challenge yourself to reach the finish or play with someone else. You have to throw the exact number to finish.
- Throw the die and move forward that number of spaces. When you land on a word you must pronounce it and say what it means in English. If you can't, you have to go back to the square you came from.

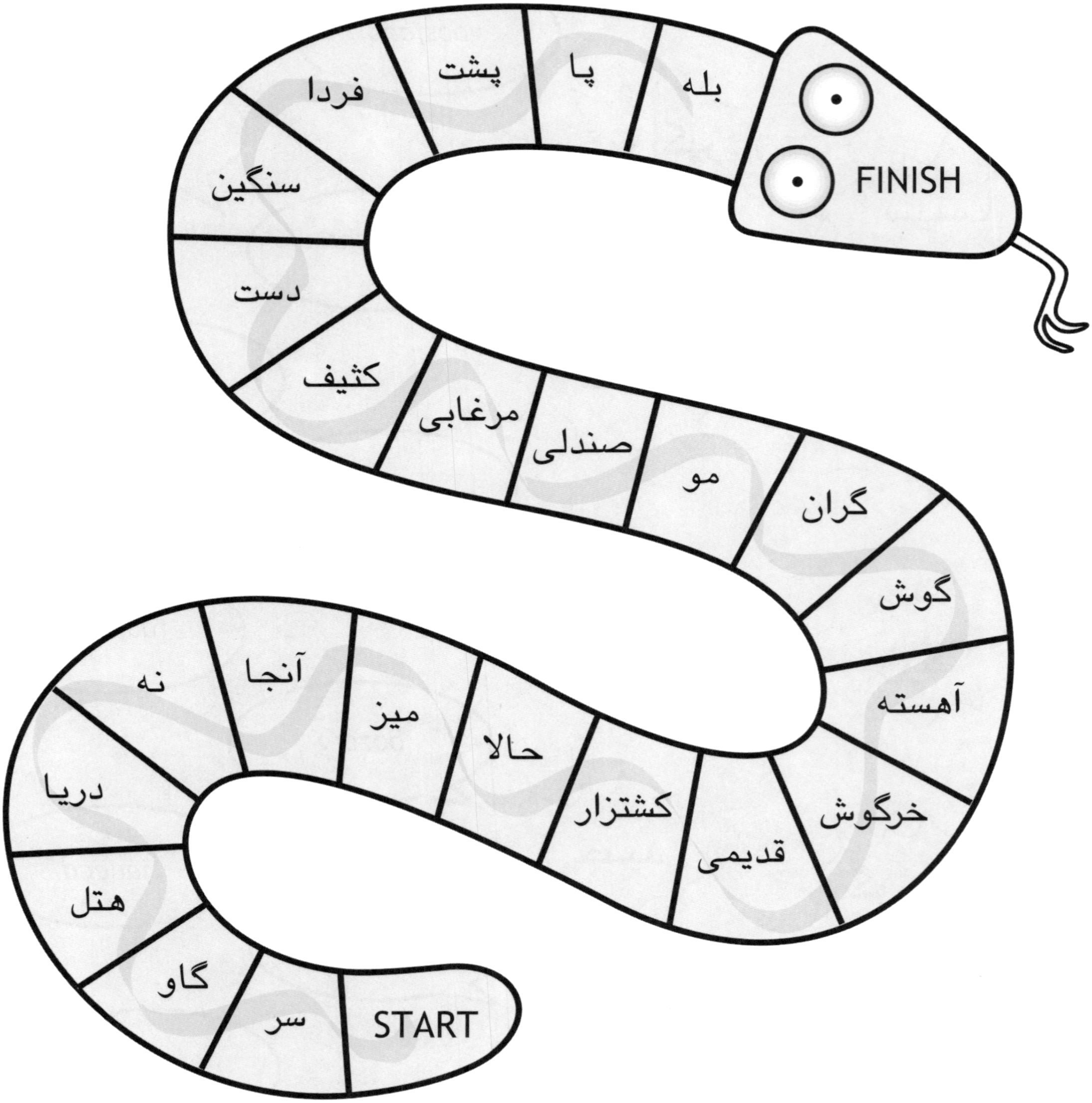

Answers

❶ Around the Home

Page 10 (top)
See page 9 for correct picture.

Page 10 (bottom)

door	در
cupboard	قفسه
stove	خوراکپز
bed	تخت خواب
table	میز
chair	صَندَلی
fridge	یخچال
computer	کامپیوتر

Page 11 (top)

میز	*meez*
قفسه	*ghafaseh*
کامپیوتر	*kaampyooter*
تخت خواب	*takhteh khaab*
پنجره	*panjareh*
تلفن	*telefon*
تلویزیون	*televeezyon*
صَندَلی	*sandalee*

Page 11 (bottom)

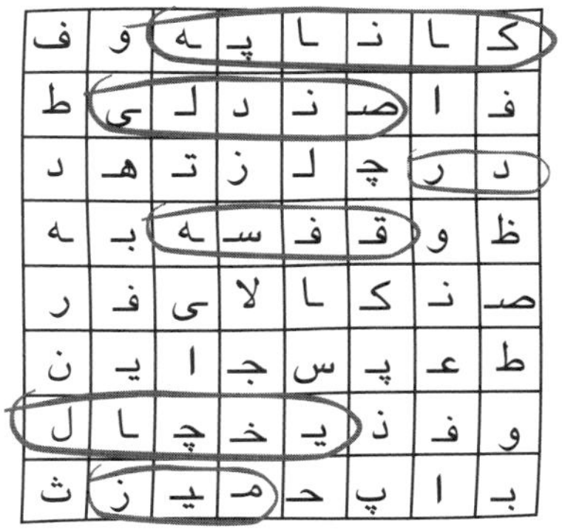

Page 12

Page 13
English word: window

❷ Clothes

Page 15 (top)

پیراهن زنانه	*peeraahaneh zanaaneh*
شورت	*short*
کفش	*kafsh*
کمربند	*kamarband*
پیراهن مردانه	*peeraahaneh mardaaneh*
تی شرت	*tee shert*
کلاه	*kolaah*
جوراب	*jooraab*

Page 15 (bottom)

Page 16

hat	کلاه	*kolaah*
shoe	کفش	*kafsh*
sock	جوراب	*jooraab*
shorts	شورت	*short*
t-shirt	تی شرت	*tee shert*
belt	کمربند	*kamarband*
coat	پالتو	*paalto*
trousers	شلوار	*shalvaar*

Page 17

کلاه (hat)	2
پالتو (coat)	0
کمربند (belt)	2
کفش (shoe)	2 (1 pair)
شلوار (trousers)	0
شورت (shorts)	2
پیراهن زنانه (dress)	1
جوراب (sock)	6 (3 pairs)
دامن (skirt)	1
تی شرت (t-shirt)	3
پیراهن مردانه (shirt)	0
پولیور (sweater)	1

Page 18

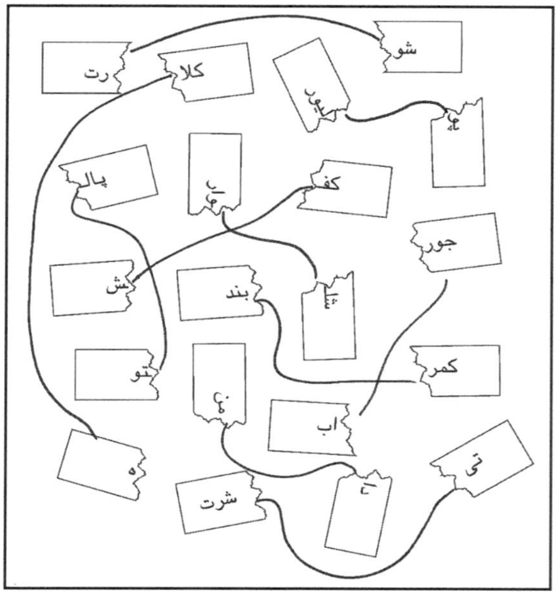

❸ Around town

Page 20 (top)

cinema	سینما
shop	فروشگاه
hotel	هتل
taxi	تاکسی
car	ماشین
train	قطار
school	مدرسه
house	خانه

Page 20 (bottom)

bicycle	4
taxi	7
house	2
train	6
bus	1
road	3
car	5

Page 21

Page 22

English word: school

Page 23

اتوبوس	*otoboos*
تاکسی	*taaksee*
مدرسه	*madreseh*
ماشین	*maasheen*
هتل	*hotel*
خانه	*khaneh*
دوچرخه	*docharkheh*
قطار	*ghataar*
فروشگاه	*forooshgaah*
سینما	*seenemaa*
رستوران	*restooraan*
جاده	*jaaddeh*

❹ Countryside

Page 25

See page 24 for correct picture.

Page 26

پل	✔	کشتزار	✔
درخت	✔	جنگل	✔
بیابان	✘	دریاچه	✘
تپه	✔	رود	✔
کوه	✔	گل	✔
دریا	✘	مزرعه	✔

Page 27 (top)

کوه	*kooh*
رود	*rood*
جنگل	*jangal*
بیابان	*biaabaan*
دریا	*daryaa*
مزرعه	*mazra`eh*
پل	*pol*
کشتزار	*keshtzaar*

Page 27 (bottom)

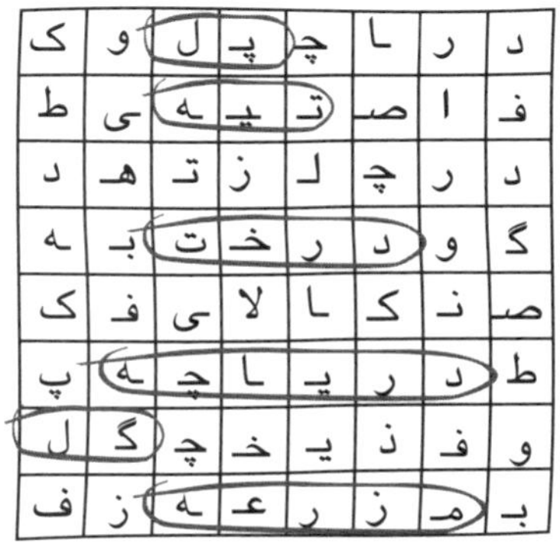

Page 28

sea	دریا	*daryaa*
lake	دریاچه	*daryaacheh*
desert	بیابان	*biaabaan*
farm	مزرعه	*mazra`eh*
flower	گل	*gol*
mountain	کوه	*kooh*
river	رود	*rood*
field	کشتزار	*keshtzaar*

❺ Opposites

Page 30

expensive	گران
big	بزرگ
light	سبک
slow	آهسته
clean	تمیز
cheap	ارزان
dirty	کثیف
small	کوچک
heavy	سنگین
new	جدید
fast	تند
old	قدیمی

Page 31
English word: change

Page 32
Odd one outs are those which are not opposites:
سنگین
کوچک
جدید
کثیف
آهسته
ارزان

Page 33

old	جدید
big	کوچک
new	قدیمی
slow	تند
dirty	تمیز
small	بزرگ
heavy	سبک
clean	کثیف
light	سنگین
expensive	ارزان
cheap	گران

❻ Animals

Page 35

گاو
خرگوش
ماهی
شیر
گوسفند
سگ
میمون
اسب
موش
گربه

Page 36

خرگوش	*khargoosh*
اسب	*asb*
میمون	*meimoon*
سگ	*sag*
گربه	*gorbeh*
موش	*moosh*
مرغابی	*morghaabee*
ماهی	*maahee*
شیر	*sheer*
گوسفند	*goosfand*
گاو	*gaav*
فیل	*feel*

Page 37

elephant	✔	mouse	✘
monkey	✘	cat	✔
sheep	✔	dog	✘
lion	✔	cow	✔
fish	✔	horse	✘
duck	✘	rabbit	✔

Page 38

monkey	میمون
cow	گاو
mouse	موش
dog	سگ
sheep	گوسفند
fish	ماهی
lion	شیر
elephant	فیل
cat	گربه
duck	مرغابی
rabbit	خرگوش
horse	اسب

❼ Parts of the Body

Page 40

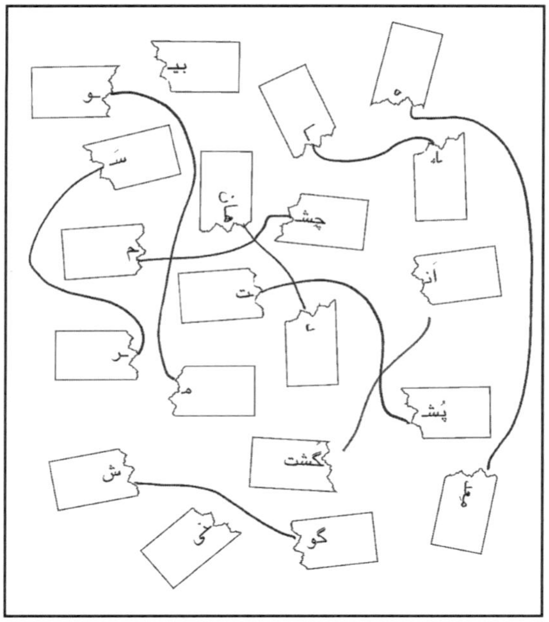

Page 41 (top)

You should have also drawn pictures of:
leg; mouth; ear; nose; eye; hair

Page 41 (bottom)

سر	*sar*
گوش	*goosh*
معده	*me`deh*
بینی	*beenee*
بازو	*baazoo*
دهان	*dahaan*
چشم	*cheshm*
پشت	*posht*

Page 42

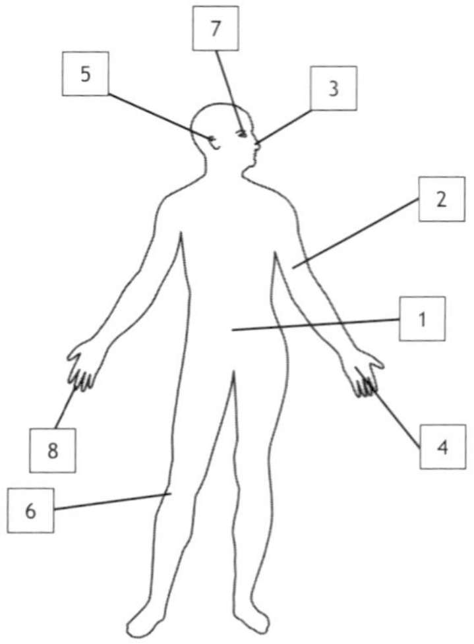

1. معده	*me`deh*
2. بینی	*beenee*
3. گوش	*goosh*
4. چشم	*cheshm*
5. بازو	*baazoo*
6. دست	*dast*
7. پا	*paa*
8. انگشت	*angosht*

Page 43

ear	گوش	*goosh*
hair	مو	*moo*
hand	دست	*dast*
stomach	معده	*me`deh*
arm	بازو	*baazoo*
back	پشت	*posht*
finger	انگشت	*angosht*
leg	پا	*paa*

8 USEFUL EXPRESSIONS

Page 45 (top)

great!	عالی!
yes	بله
yesterday	دیروز
where?	کجا؟
today	امروز
here	اینجا
please	لطفا
no	نه

Page 45 (bottom)

آنجا	*aanjaa*
سلام	*salaam*
فردا	*fardaa*
خدا حافظ	*khodaa haafez*
چند؟	*chand?*
ممنون	*mamnoon*
ببخشید	*bebakhsheed*
عالی!	*aalee!*

Page 46

English word: please

Page 47

Page 48

yes	بله	*baleh*
hello	سلام	*salaam*
no	نه	*na*
sorry	ببخشید	*bebakhsheed*
please	لطفا	*lotfan*
there	آنجا	*aanjaa*
thank you	ممنون	*mamnoon*
tomorrow	فردا	*fardaa*

ROUND-UP

Page 49

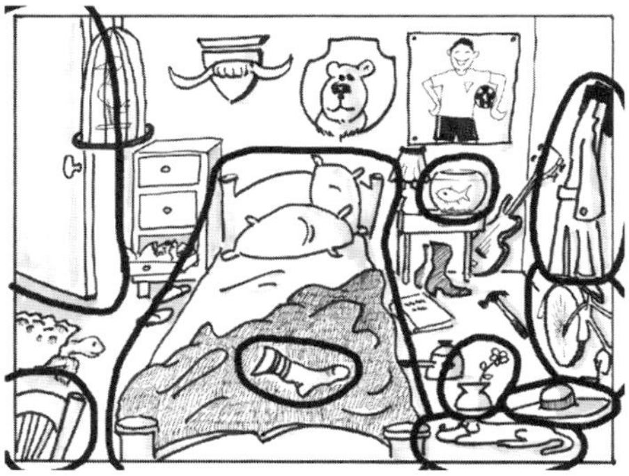

Page 50

Page 51

میز (Because it isn't an animal.)
تلفن (Because it isn't a means of transportation.)
کشتزار (Because it isn't an item of clothing.)
درخت (Because it isn't connected with water.)
سینما (Because it isn't a descriptive word.)
ماهی (Because it lives in water/doesn't have legs.)
کاناپه (Because it isn't a part of the body.)
لطفاً (Because it isn't an expression of time.)
تخت خواب (Because you wouldn't find it in the kitchen.)

Page 52

Words that appear in the picture:

تی شرت
ماشین
گل
کفش
قطار
میمون
تلویزیون
صندلی
کمربند
شورت

Page 53

sweater	پولیور	*buloofir*
lake	دریاچه	*daryaacheh*
thank you	ممنون	*mamnoon*
bed	تخت خواب	*takhteh khaab*
house	خانه	*khaaneh*
forest	جنگل	*jangal*
where?	کجا؟	*kojaa?*
heavy	سنگین	*sangeen*

Page 54

English phrase: well done!

Page 55

شورت	✔ (shade)
تی شرت	✘
در	✔ (handle)
گربه	✘
صندلی	✔ (back)
ماهی	✔ (direction)
جوراب	✔ (pattern)
سگ	✘

Page 56

fridge	یخچال
trousers	شلوار
shop	فروشگاه
school	مدرسه
river	رود
great!	عالی!
small	کوچک
light	سبک
arm	بازو
stomach	معده
clean	تمیز
horse	اسب

Page 57

سلام	*salaam*
دیروز	*deerooz*
خوراکپز	*khoraakpaz*
سینما	*seenemaa*
تاکسی	*taaksee*
کوه	*kooh*
کشتزار	*keshtzaar*
بزرگ	*bozorg*
جدید	*jadeed*
گوسفند	*goosfand*
انگشت	*angosht*
فیل	*feel*

Page 58

Here are the English equivalents and pronunciation of the words, in order from START to FINISH:

head *sar*	farm *mazra`eh*	duck *morghaabee*
cow *gaav*	old *ghadeemee*	dirty *kaseef*
hotel *hotel*	rabbit *khargoosh*	hand *dast*
sea *daryaa*	slow *aahesteh*	heavy *sangeen*
no *na*	ear *goosh*	tomorrow *fardaa*
there *aanjaa*	expensive *geraan*	back *posht*
table *meez*	hair *moo*	leg *paa*
now *haalaa*	chair *sandalee*	yes *baleh*

پنجره

panjareh

کامپیوتر

kaampyooter

قفسه

ghafaseh

میز

meez

صندلی

sandalee

یخچال

yakhchaal

خوراکپز

khoraakpaz

کاناپه

kaanaapeh

تخت خواب

takhteh khaab

در

dar

تلویزیون

televeezyon

تلفن

telefon

window

computer

cupboard

table

chair

fridge

stove

sofa

bed

door

television

telephone

کمربند

kamarband

پالتو

paalto

دامن

daaman

کلاه

kolaah

تی شرت

tee shert

کفش

kafsh

پولیور

poleever

پیراهن مردانه

peeraahaneh mardaaneh

شورت

short

جوراب

jooraab

شلوار

shalvaar

پیراهن زنانه

peeraahaneh zanaaneh

coat	belt
hat	skirt
shoe	t-shirt
shirt	sweater
sock	shorts
dress	trousers

ماشین

maasheen

مدرسه

madreseh

سینما

seenemaa

جاده

jaaddeh

فروشگاه

forooshgaah

هتل

hotel

دوچرخه

docharkheh

تاکسی

taaksee

اتوبوس

otoboos

رستوران

restooraan

خانه

khaaneh

قطار

ghataar

car

school

cinema

road

shop

hotel

bicycle

taxi

bus

restaurant

house

train

جنگل

jangal

دریاچه

daryaacheh

دریا

daryaa

تپه

tappeh

درخت

derakht

کوه

kooh

گل

gol

بیابان

biaabaan

رود

rood

پل

pol

کشتزار

keshtzaar

مزرعه

mazra`eh

forest	lake
sea	hill
tree	mountain
flower	desert
river	bridge
field	farm

سنگین

sangeen

سبک

sabok

بزرگ

bozorg

کوچک

koochek

قدیمی

ghadeemee

جدید

jadeed

تند

tond

آهسته

aahesteh

تمیز

tameez

کثیف

kaseef

ارزان

arzaan

گران

geraan

light

heavy

small

big

new

old

slow

fast

dirty

clean

expensive

cheap

مرغابی

morghaabee

گربه

gorbeh

موش

moosh

گاو

gaav

خرگوش

khargoosh

سگ

sag

اسب

asb

میمون

meimoon

شیر

sheer

ماهی

maahee

فیل

feel

گوسفند

goosfand

cat	duck
cow	mouse
dog	rabbit
monkey	horse
fish	lion
sheep	elephant

بازو

baazoo

انگشت

angosht

سر

sar

دهان

dahaan

گوش

goosh

پا

paa

دست

dast

معده

me`deh

چشم

cheshm

مو

moo

بینی

beenee

پشت

posht

finger

arm

mouth

head

leg

ear

stomach

hand

hair

eye

back

nose

لطفاً
lotfan

ممنون
mamnoon

بله
baleh

نه
na

سلام
salaam

خدا حافظ
khodaa haafez

دیروز
deerooz

امروز
emrooz

فردا
fardaa

کجا؟
kojaa?

اینجا
eenjaa

آنجا
aanjaa

ببخشید!
bebakhsheed!

چند؟
chand?

عالی!
aalee!

حالا
haalaa

thank you	please
no	yes
goodbye	hello
today	yesterday
where?	tomorrow
there	here
how much?	sorry!
now	great!